BLUEPRINTS
The Tables Book

Rod Bosanko

Stanley Thornes (Publishers) Ltd

Stanley Thornes for TEACHERS:
BLUEPRINTS • PRIMARY COLOURS • LEARNING TARGETS

Stanley Thornes for Teachers publishes practical teacher's ideas books and photocopiable resources for use in primary schools. Our three key series, **Blueprints**, **Primary Colours** and **Learning Targets** together provide busy teachers with unbeatable curriculum coverage, inspiration and value for money. We mail teachers and schools about our books regularly. To join the mailing list simply photocopy and complete the form below and return using the **FREEPOST** address to receive regular updates on our new and existing titles. You may also like to add the name of a friend who would be interested in being on the mailing list. Books can be bought by credit card over the telephone and information obtained on (01242) 267280.

Please add my name to the **Stanley Thornes for TEACHERS** mailing list.

Mr/Mrs/Miss/Ms _____

Address _____

_____ postcode _____

School address _____

_____ postcode _____

Please also send information about **Stanley Thornes for TEACHERS** to:

Mr/Mrs/Miss/Ms _____

Address _____

_____ postcode _____

To: Marketing Services Dept., Stanley Thornes Ltd, FREEPOST (GR 782), Cheltenham, GL50 1BR

Text © Rod Bosanko 1996
Original line illustrations by Debbie Clark © STP, 1996

The author would like to dedicate this book to his wife, Susan. The author acknowledges with thanks the help and support of the headteacher, staff and children of Severne Primary School, Acocks Green, Birmingham.

First published in 1996
First published in new binding in 1998 by:
Stanley Thornes (Publishers) Ltd
Ellenborough House, Wellington Street
CHELTENHAM GL50 1YW
England

A catalogue record for this book is available from the British Library.

ISBN 0–7487–3462–7

Typeset by Tech-Set, Gateshead, Tyne & Wear
Printed and bound in Great Britain by Redwood Books, Trowbridge, Wiltshire

99 00 01 02 / 10 9 8 7 6 5 4 3 2

CONTENTS

INTRODUCTION

The Tables Book is a comprehensive and original photocopiable compendium of 118 pages of activities and games designed to teach the multiplication tables. It can be used on its own or alongside any mathematics scheme. Its aim is to develop a child's numeracy through practice, to increase memory skills and to build self-confidence.

Most primary schools will have banks of mathematical equipment and activities, either bought or home-made, to support their number programmes. This book provides a huge bank of such material ready-made for use in the classroom, saving you both time and money. It allows you to prepare carefully graded, relevant activities and games at a fraction of the cost of commercially purchased material. It also means that a lost piece does not cause problems: you simply photocopy the sheet again and replace the piece.

The activities are highly versatile. They can be photocopied directly onto card or photocopied onto paper and stuck onto card. They may be coloured and covered for permanent use, or quickly run off on paper for more immediate classroom use. You will find practical instructions in the next section 'Making and using the activities'. Manufacture of the materials is an ideal activity both for parent helpers and for children themselves either at home or at school. My present class of Year 2 infants are certainly capable of producing their own books. As the cost of producing the activities is minimal, you can even send them home to be made up and practiced with parents.

The Tables Book aims to provide a wide variety of interesting, motivating and self-checking activities which will help children to learn their tables. Repetition of discovered information is a key factor in learning tables, but it is this that children often find tedious. As they work through each of the activities in the book the repetition necessary for learning tables is disguised, firstly by the intrinsic interest of the material, secondly by a sense of ownership of the material, and finally by the way it is presented. Most of the activities can be made into booklets complete with covers, progress charts or graphs. Self-awarded achievement certificates, medals and stars are included. The children can colour the sheets in and personalise their work, and build up their own library of tables books which also serve as a progress record for the teacher. Alternatively, the activities may be used as individual worksheets.

The Tables Book covers the following tables:

- Tables 0 to 12 Times tables (reference resource)
- Tables 0 to 12 Tables challenge/Solitaire
- Tables 0 to 12: Going dotty!
- Tables 2 to 12: Count and colour tables
- Tables 1 to 12: Mini tables books
- Tables 1 to 12: Tables mazes
- Tables 0 to 12: Hard tables test
- Tables 2 to 12: Tables puzzles
- Tables 2 to 12: Thinking backwards
- Tables 1 to 12: Tables slider cards
- Tables 0 to 12: Tables grid cards

You will find an overview of the skills coverage of each section in the Overview of Tables Skills on page v. Nought- and one-times tables are important and often ignored concepts, so they are included as an integral part of the work in this book.

Most of the activities can be used flexibly with either individuals or groups. They are graded in a developmental order from the front to the back of the book. At the front there is a strong self-check and support element to the activities. As you go further, the activities rely increasingly on memory, research skills and speed.

Throughout the book the children are given a variety of graded strategies which the teacher can re-use or amend until each table is secure. However, the principal strategy underlying all the activities within the book is this: that when children get something wrong it needs to be said repeatedly until it is memorised. For example, in the two-times table, if the child gets four times two wrong or doesn't know it, she or he should say it a dozen or so times until it sticks in their head: e.g. "Four twos are eight, Four twos are eight", etc.

Saying the whole table all the way through just once gives only one exposure to the error, which is not effective. Focusing on the error repeatedly in the way already described will gradually correct it.

Able young children and older children with special educational needs can use the material as well, and the teacher will be able to select the material accordingly. The 'open typeface' numerals used in most of the activities provide an extra opportunity to help those children who have difficulty in forming their numbers because they can trace inside the digits. This will also help children who reverse their numbers. Other children will simply enjoy colouring in the numbers and in so doing will become more familiar with them.

All of these activities have been extensively trialled and used by real children in real classrooms over a number of years. They are stimulating, fun to do and highly successful. Once you have started to work with the activities we think you will find this book an absolutely invaluable resource to return to again and again.

OVERVIEW OF TABLES SKILLS

In all the activities, children practice a wide spectrum of number skills. Some skills are quite basic: digit formation, number progression, number pattern and so on. Other skills are high order skills which require memory recall, logical thought, speed and accuracy.

All the activities provide interest and involvement in what can be a tedious process for children. It is the interest factor provided by this material which helps children to enjoy repetition and thereby enjoy learning their tables.

Tables 0–12 Copymasters 1–7
A reference source which can be a book or a wall display.

Tables 0–12 Copymasters 8–21
These activities are self-checking and self-correcting. Children actually throw away the cards they know and keep the ones they aren't sure about. In this way the children only has to practise the tables he or she needs to. Speed and accuracy are important skills here. There are many other ways of using this resource, for example 'snap'.

Tables 0–12 Copymasters 22–35
Counting, counting on, addition and multiplication are all skills which are practised in this section.

Tables 2–12 Copymasters 36–47
Counting on in regular intervals, for example 3s, 4s etc. Number sequencing, number patterns, prediction.

Tables 1–12 Copymasters 48–51
A reference source which easily fits into pockets and pencil cases.

Tables 1–12 Copymasters 52–65
Using reference sources and previously practised skills, the children have to find their way through a maze to answer a question. Self-checking and self-correcting. Scope is provided for the children to make up their own mazes for a friend to do.

Tables 0–12 Copymasters 66–79
Previous skill and knowledge are practised in these random-order activities. Self-checking can be carried out using reference material. Speed is a factor.

Tables 2–12 Copymasters 80–86
Previous skill and knowledge, and the use of reference material, are practised in this section. The children find patterns which are regular and provide an element of self-checking. There is also scope for the children to make up their own puzzles for a friend.

Tables 2–12 Copymasters 87–98
Children use previous skill and knowledge, and available reference material, to solve the puzzles and write the tables.

Tables 1–12 Copymasters 99–111
Random recall, speed, accuracy and memory are important factors in this activity. There are four different tests for each table so that the children have to think for themselves. An ongoing activity which is self-checking and self-correcting.

Tables 0–12 Copymasters 112–118
A high order of skill is practised and developed in this activity. Speed and accuracy are required in this 169-question, random-order test. There are four different self-checking, self-correcting activities. The results are recorded on a progress graph and there are certificates to reward achievement.

GENERAL INSTRUCTIONS

The activities in this book can be prepared in three ways:
a) photocopied directly onto card;
b) photocopied onto paper;
c) as in b) and then glued onto card.

Preparation
1 Photocopy the copymasters as required.
2 Copies can be coloured and either made into books, used as single sheets or mounted as wall displays.
3 Games may be stored in envelopes which can be decorated and personalised.

4 You can laminate copies if you wish, using transparent adhesive plastic, e.g. Coverlon®.
6 On sets of copies you can run a wide felt-tipped pen around the edge to colour-code them. If the pen is used half on and half off the sheet no ruler is necessary. This technique may require some practice but it is quite effective. Each complete set should be edged with the same coloured pen so that pieces can be returned to their correct places easily. Books can be easily identified by their coloured borders.

MAKING AND PLAYING THE GAMES

Times tables
Copymasters 1–7
An activity for one child (booklets) or groups of children (wall display).

Objective of the activity
To provide a reference source of all the multiplication tables from 0- to 12-times.

Preparation
a) Photocopy the required copymasters onto paper.
b) Each sheet is coloured in and decorated. The book comes complete with cover for colouring and personalising, and margin spaces have been left around the tables so children can decorate these too. Children can use felt-tipped pens because in this form the felt-tip colours don't spoil the other pages.
c) Fold each sheet in half backwards.
d) When all sheets are complete they can be stapled into a book as shown below.

To use the activity
It can be used as a mounted wall display and/or as a personal reference book for individual children.

Tables challenge/ Solitaire
Copymasters 8–21
Two activities — one for one child and the other for two children.

Objective of the activities
To build up a child's self-confidence by providing a self-correcting method of learning tables facts (Solitaire) and a partnered version of the same game (Tables challenge).

Preparation
a) Photocopy copymasters 9–21 onto paper or card to provide one set of cards for each table from 1-times to 12-times.
b) Colour the copies.
c) Cut the copymasters along all of the solid lines.
d) Fold each of the components along the dotted lines.

Copymaster 8 is a pattern for making two envelopes to store each set of tables cards separately from the others. (You will need 12 altogether.)
a) Photocopy and cut out along the solid lines. Fold along the dotted lines and continue as shown.

b) Write the number of the set of tables to be stored in the envelope in the box on the front of the envelope.
c) Colour and personalise.

To use the activities
METHOD A (2 CHILDREN): TABLES CHALLENGE
1 The folded cards are stood on a table with the questions facing one child, and the answers facing another child.
2 One child touches or points at one of the cards and says, for example, "One times two is...two".
3 The partner then tells them if they are right or wrong.
4 If a child answers the question correctly they keep the card; if a wrong answer is given, the cards are turned around and learnt.
5 The game is played over and over until a child can 'win' all the cards.
6 The children take it in turns to try to win all of the cards without making a mistake.

METHOD B (1 CHILD): SOLITAIRE
1 The cards are folded flat, clipped with a paper-clip, mixed up and spread out on the table question-side up.
2 The child reads the question and gives the answer; for example, "One times two...is two". Then they turn the card over to check the answer.
3 If the child's answer is correct, they can keep the card. If it is wrong, or they failed to answer at all, the card is replaced. Then the child practices the question before starting all over again.
4 The game is over when all the cards have been picked up in succession with no mistakes or omissions.

Going dotty!
Copymasters 22–35
An activity for one child.

Objective of the activity
To show the children how a table builds in multiples of discrete numbers. They will learn that the next answer in a table can be found by adding one more 'pile' of that number to the previous total.

Preparation
a) Photocopy the copymasters onto paper.
b) These can be stapled together in book form or used as single sheets.

To use the activity
1 Each child draws the required number of spots into the required number of boxes.
2 The total number of spots in each line should be counted and the equation at the end of the line completed.
3 The table is then practiced and learnt.
4 If used in book form, the children can colour and personalise the cover.

Count and colour tables
Copymasters 36–47

Objective of the activity
To give the children experience in counting on in regular intervals and seeing that there is a pattern which can be predicted. This pattern is directly related to each table.

Preparation
a) Photocopy the copymasters and the cover onto paper.
b) These can be stapled together in book form, or used as single sheets.

To use the activity
1 Using the grids on the left-hand side of the sheets, children count every second box for the 2-times table and colour them in. Then they count every third box for the 3-times table and colour them in, and so on.
2 A pattern begins to emerge which is different for each sheet. Sometimes the children can predict the pattern without counting on.
3 From the pattern and the sequence of numbers, the table on the right-hand side of each sheet can be completed and learnt.
4 There is an award system on the front cover (copymaster 36). Children colour in the number star which corresponds to the table they can say without looking.
5 Friends could test each other to check that they can say the table without looking.

Mini tables book
Copymasters 48–51
A set of reference booklets for the children.

Objective of the booklets
To provide children with four pocket-sized reference and practice books covering all the tables from 1 to 12, with an award system on each back cover.

Preparation
There are four eight-page books to make for each child. Each book covers three tables with three practice spaces per sheet.
a) Photocopy the required copymasters onto paper.
b) Trim the edges off the paper along the bold lines.
c) Fold and cut each sheet as indicated in the following diagrams.

To use the booklets
1 Each of the four booklets contains three tables printed in full. Opposite each table there is a blank page which the children use to write the table out again for themselves.

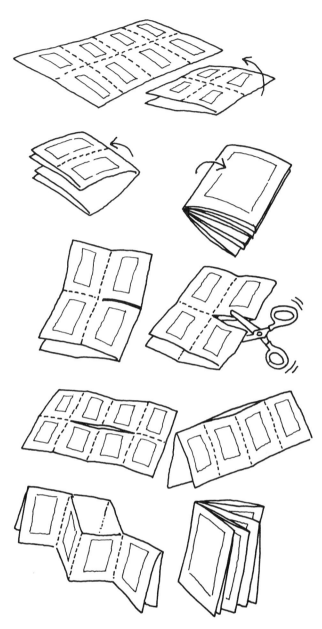

2 Children can colour and personalise the cover and individual pages.
3 The books are small enough to be kept in pockets, pencil cases, etc. The children can keep them handy for their own personal reference and practice. They can also be used for one child to help another to practice a given table.
4 The books can be taken home and used for practice with parents.
5 The award system on the back cover can be used for encouragement.

[My Year 2 students enjoy making these booklets for themselves. They become quite attached to them, and when they become tatty, they make themselves a new set.]

Tables mazes books
Copymasters 52–65
An activity for one child.

Objective of the activity
To give children tables practice in an activity which is interesting and self-checking. The tables (0- to 12-

times) questions are presented in random numerical order and the children have to put them into the correct numerical order.

Preparation
a) Photocopy the required copymasters onto paper.
b) These can be stapled together in book form or used as single sheets.

To use the activity
1 Children use coloured pencils to trace their way through each maze from the questions to the answers.
2 Using the first workspace at the bottom of the page, they sort the questions and answers from the maze into correct numerical order. Two of the lines in this workspace are filled in to give them some guidance.
3 There are two blank workspaces for the children to write out the table again.
4 Children can colour and personalise the cover and sheets.
5 More-able children can use the blank sheet (copymaster 65) to make up their own maze for a friend to play.

Hard tables test
Copymasters 66–79 and page x
An activity for one child.

Objective of the activity
To provide practice of multiplication tables from 0- to 12-times in the form of random testing.

Preparation
a) Photocopy the required copymasters onto paper.
b) If the table tests are to be used as separate sheets, cut the copymasters in half along the dotted lines. Alternatively, fold and make the set of copymasters into a book as per the instructions for **Times tables** (copymasters 1–7).

Note: Keep a copy of page x separate. This is a certificate children can award themselves when they have completed the 'How well did you do?' record sheet (copymaster 66).

To use the activity
1 Younger or less-able children can work with separate sheets or with a book that only contains only one or two tables to begin with.
2 Children should complete test A of any given table first. After checking their answers and scoring themselves in the box provided, they should learn any they did not know before moving on to test B.
3 If they get all 13 correct, they can colour in one of the boxes for the relevant table on the 'How well did you do?' record sheet.
4 When children have completed five totally correct tests and filled in all of the boxes on any line of the 'How well did you do?' record sheet, they can award themselves a certificate (page x).
5 To make this harder, the activity could be timed. Or it can be used with the back-up of a reference table in which the process of looking-up an answer becomes a learning activity in itself.

Tables puzzles
Copymasters 80–86
An activity for one child.

Objective of the activity
To give children an opportunity to use their acquired knowledge of tables to solve a puzzle and reveal a pattern. They can also use research skills to look up information.

Preparation
a) Photocopy the required sheets onto paper.
b) These can be folded up and assembled into book form as described in **Times tables** (copymasters 1–7), or they can be used as separate sheets.

To use the activity
1 The children look at 25 different numbers in a box and colour in only the numbers which are in the answers for that particular table. They can use one of the printed tables to help them if they have difficulty.
2 A pattern is revealed which is easy to check.
3 Children then write out the tables in correct numerical order in the first of the two workspaces.
4 Using the second workspace, they write out the table without looking at the box above.
5 Copymaster 86 is a blank sheet for them to make up their own puzzles for friends to do.
6 The sheets can be coloured and personalised.

Thinking backwards
Copymasters 87–98

Objective of the activity
To give tables practice in which children have to work backwards from the answers.

Preparation
a) Photocopy the required sheets onto paper.
b) The pages can be used as separate sheets or stapled together (not folded) into book form complete with cover.

To use the activity
1 The children complete the equations by working out, for instance, "How many twos make six?" They can rely on memory or refer to tables charts to answer the questions.
2 The children can then write the table out in correct numerical order in the workspace provided.
3 The pages/book can be coloured and personalised.

Tables slider cards
Copymasters 99–111
An activity for one child.

Objective of the activity
To provide tables practice through the testing of each table, from the 1-times to the 12-times table, in four different random orders. There are six slider test cards for each child giving a total of 48 different tables tests.

Preparation
a) Photocopy the required copymasters onto card. Note that for each table there is a specific front cover and a matched sliding page. You must be careful to use

the correct pair of pages together. For each table you will also need a back cover (copymaster 105). This is a record sheet and is not specific to any particular table. So, for example, for the 1-times and 2-times table slider set you would need to photocopy onto card copymasters 99, 105 and 106.

b) Cut out each sheet along the printed outline.

c) Score and fold back the shaded area on the front slider card sheets (99–104).

d) Carefully cut out the four windows on the front of each slider sheet (99–104 again). This could be done by a parent helper using a sharp knife and safety ruler.

e) Carefully glue the fronts and backs together as shown below to make an envelope/wallet.

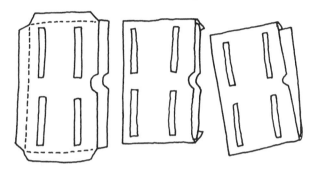

f) Carefully push the slider cards (copymasters 106–111) inside the wallets (iii).

g) When the slider cards are pushed right into the wallets you will see that for each of the two tables on every sheet, there is an 'A' at the top followed by a column of numbers in the QUESTIONS column window. The ANSWERS column is empty.

To use the activity

1 Children align a piece of lined paper with the lines in the middle of the card and make sure that the answers are covered up.

2 Test A, B, C or D is selected and the children write the answers to the test on the piece of paper.

3 When the test is completed they can self-check, learn and try again.

These tests can be used over and over again until the tables gradually become clearer in the children's minds. The tests can also be timed to make them more challenging.

Tables grid cards
Copymasters 112–118
A class test activity.

Objective of the activity

To build upon the experience the children have gained so far, first in dealing with tables in numerical order and then in random order for each table, and to combine all of the tables from 0- to 12-times in four different random grids.

Preparation

a) Photocopy the required copymasters onto card and cut out along the printed outline. There are two question sheet copymasters and two answer sheet copymasters. Tables grid A and B (112) goes with

tables grid A and B answers (114); tables grid C and D (113) goes with tables grid C and D answers (115).

b) Trim off the left-hand edge where indicated.

c) Using a sharp knife and safety ruler cut out the two windows on the question sheet. (A parent helper could do this for you.)

d) Fold and score the dotted line on the question sheet and glue it to the answer sheet so that the box of numbers fits centrally in each window.

e) Photocopy copymaster 116. This is the pupil worksheet. Trim off the left-hand edge where indicated.

f) Photocopy copymaster 117. Cut it out and stick onto the back of one of the grid card folder.

g) Photocopy copymaster 118. Cut it out and stick it onto the back of the other grid card folder.

To use the activity

1 The test is administered when all the children have their grid card folders with their worksheets inserted into the question and answer folder, thereby covering the answers on the back page.

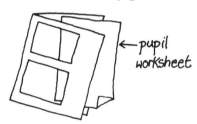
←pupil worksheet

2 The teacher then selects one of the four tests, A, B, C or D. The children are told that the test is to be timed over 20 minutes and that they should record when they finish if they complete the test within that time. This can be done in two ways. As the children work, the teacher could tell them the time every minute. If a child finishes after the teacher has just said, say, "Eleven minutes", that child should record that they finished within twelve minutes. A different way of timing is for each child to whisper "Finished" when they have completed the test. The teacher can then tell them their time in minutes and seconds.

3 Children could hold a blank sheet of card across and down the grid so they can see more clearly which numbers should be multiplied against each other.

4 When the test is over, the children remove their worksheets revealing the answer grids against which they can check their answers. They then fill in their scores and times on the pupil answer sheets.

5 Any wrong answers should be learnt before the next test.

6 The children draw a graph of their progress and they can award themselves any 'medal' that they win.

7 Children can colour and personalise their own cards and sheets.

Well done!

Name: _____

Signed: _____

CERTIFICATE
OF
BEING GREAT!

This certificate is awarded to

_ _ _ _ _ _ _ _ _ _ _

for

_ _ _ _ _ _ _ _ _ _ _

_ _ _ _ _ _ _ _ _ _ _

Signed: _____

0-times table

0 × 0 = 0
1 × 0 = 0
2 × 0 = 0
3 × 0 = 0
4 × 0 = 0
5 × 0 = 0
6 × 0 = 0
7 × 0 = 0
8 × 0 = 0
9 × 0 = 0
10 × 0 = 0
11 × 0 = 0
12 × 0 = 0

Times Tables

2-times table

0	× 2 =	0
1	× 2 =	2
2	× 2 =	4
3	× 2 =	6
4	× 2 =	8
5	× 2 =	10
6	× 2 =	12
7	× 2 =	14
8	× 2 =	16
9	× 2 =	18
10	× 2 =	20
11	× 2 =	22
12	× 2 =	24

1-times table

0	× 1 =	0
1	× 1 =	1
2	× 1 =	2
3	× 1 =	3
4	× 1 =	4
5	× 1 =	5
6	× 1 =	6
7	× 1 =	7
8	× 1 =	8
9	× 1 =	9
10	× 1 =	10
11	× 1 =	11
12	× 1 =	12

4-times table

0	× 4	=	0
1	× 4	=	4
2	× 4	=	8
3	× 4	=	12
4	× 4	=	16
5	× 4	=	20
6	× 4	=	24
7	× 4	=	28
8	× 4	=	32
9	× 4	=	36
10	× 4	=	40
11	× 4	=	44
12	× 4	=	48

3-times table

0	× 3	=	0
1	× 3	=	3
2	× 3	=	6
3	× 3	=	9
4	× 3	=	12
5	× 3	=	15
6	× 3	=	18
7	× 3	=	21
8	× 3	=	24
9	× 3	=	27
10	× 3	=	30
11	× 3	=	33
12	× 3	=	36

6-times table

0 × 6 = 0	
1 × 6 = 6	
2 × 6 = 12	
3 × 6 = 18	
4 × 6 = 24	
5 × 6 = 30	
6 × 6 = 36	
7 × 6 = 42	
8 × 6 = 48	
9 × 6 = 54	
10 × 6 = 60	
11 × 6 = 66	
12 × 6 = 72	

5-times table

0 × 5 = 0	
1 × 5 = 5	
2 × 5 = 10	
3 × 5 = 15	
4 × 5 = 20	
5 × 5 = 25	
6 × 5 = 30	
7 × 5 = 35	
8 × 5 = 40	
9 × 5 = 45	
10 × 5 = 50	
11 × 5 = 55	
12 × 5 = 60	

8-times table

0	× 8	=	0
1	× 8	=	8
2	× 8	=	16
3	× 8	=	24
4	× 8	=	32
5	× 8	=	40
6	× 8	=	48
7	× 8	=	56
8	× 8	=	64
9	× 8	=	72
10	× 8	=	80
11	× 8	=	88
12	× 8	=	96

7-times table

0	× 7	=	0
1	× 7	=	7
2	× 7	=	14
3	× 7	=	21
4	× 7	=	28
5	× 7	=	35
6	× 7	=	42
7	× 7	=	49
8	× 7	=	56
9	× 7	=	63
10	× 7	=	70
11	× 7	=	77
12	× 7	=	84

10-times table

0 × 10	=	0
1 × 10	=	10
2 × 10	=	20
3 × 10	=	30
4 × 10	=	40
5 × 10	=	50
6 × 10	=	60
7 × 10	=	70
8 × 10	=	80
9 × 10	=	90
10 × 10	=	100
11 × 10	=	110
12 × 10	=	120

9-times table

0 × 9	=	0
1 × 9	=	9
2 × 9	=	18
3 × 9	=	27
4 × 9	=	36
5 × 9	=	45
6 × 9	=	54
7 × 9	=	63
8 × 9	=	72
9 × 9	=	81
10 × 9	=	90
11 × 9	=	99
12 × 9	=	108

12-times table

0	× 12	=	0
1	× 12	=	12
2	× 12	=	24
3	× 12	=	36
4	× 12	=	48
5	× 12	=	60
6	× 12	=	72
7	× 12	=	84
8	× 12	=	96
9	× 12	=	108
10	× 12	=	120
11	× 12	=	132
12	× 12	=	144

11-times table

0	× 11	=	0
1	× 11	=	11
2	× 11	=	22
3	× 11	=	33
4	× 11	=	44
5	× 11	=	55
6	× 11	=	66
7	× 11	=	77
8	× 11	=	88
9	× 11	=	99
10	× 11	=	110
11	× 11	=	121
12	× 11	=	132

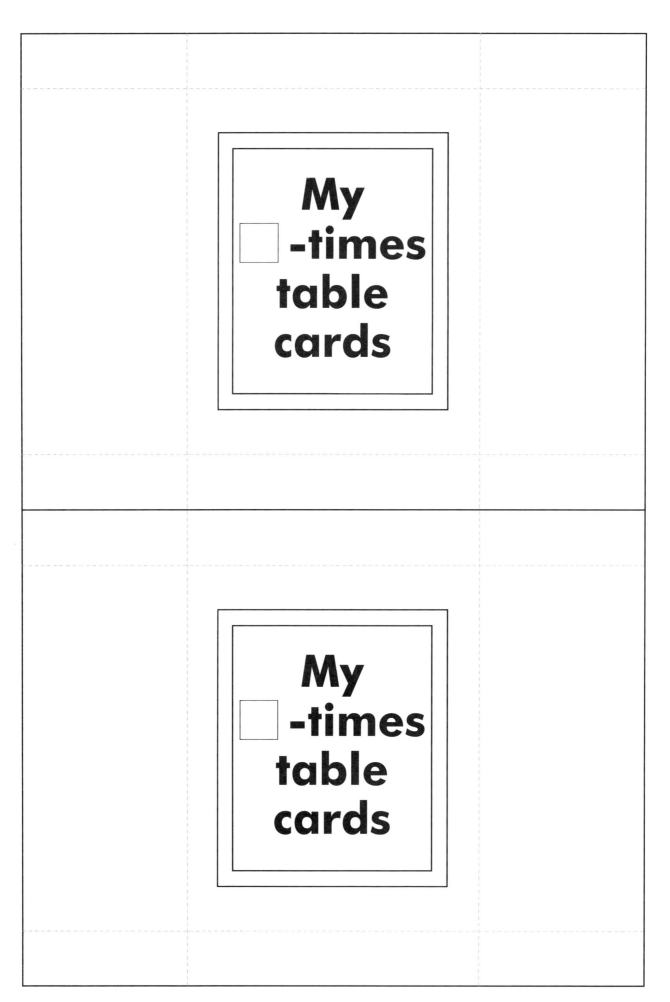

My ☐-times table cards

My ☐-times table cards

$6 \times 0 =$ 0	$12 \times 0 =$ 0
$5 \times 0 =$ 0	$11 \times 0 =$ 0
$4 \times 0 =$ 0	$10 \times 0 =$ 0
$3 \times 0 =$ 0	$9 \times 0 =$ 0
$2 \times 0 =$ 0	$8 \times 0 =$ 0
$1 \times 0 =$ 0	$7 \times 0 =$ 0

$1 \times 12 =$	$1 \times 6 =$
12	**6**
$11 \times 1 =$	$5 \times 1 =$
11	**5**
$10 \times 1 =$	$4 \times 1 =$
10	**4**
$9 \times 1 =$	$3 \times 1 =$
9	**3**
$8 \times 1 =$	$2 \times 1 =$
8	**2**
$7 \times 1 =$	$1 \times 1 =$
7	**1**

12 × 2 =	24
11 × 2 =	22
10 × 2 =	20
9 × 2 =	18
8 × 2 =	16
7 × 2 =	14
6 × 2 =	12
5 × 2 =	10
4 × 2 =	8
3 × 2 =	6
2 × 2 =	4
1 × 2 =	2

18	6 × 3 =	36	12 × 3 =
15	5 × 3 =	33	11 × 3 =
12	4 × 3 =	30	10 × 3 =
9	3 × 3 =	27	9 × 3 =
6	2 × 3 =	24	8 × 3 =
3	1 × 3 =	21	7 × 3 =

12 × 4 =	48	4 × 6 =	24
11 × 4 =	44	5 × 4 =	20
10 × 4 =	40	4 × 4 =	16
9 × 4 =	36	3 × 4 =	12
4 × 8 =	32	2 × 4 =	8
7 × 4 =	28	1 × 4 =	4

30	6 × 5 =	60	12 × 5 =
25	5 × 5 =	55	11 × 5 =
20	4 × 5 =	50	10 × 5 =
15	3 × 5 =	45	9 × 5 =
10	2 × 5 =	40	8 × 5 =
5	1 × 5 =	35	7 × 5 =

$12 \times 6 =$	72
$11 \times 6 =$	66
$10 \times 6 =$	60
$9 \times 6 =$	54
$8 \times 6 =$	48
$7 \times 6 =$	42

$6 \times 6 =$	36
$5 \times 6 =$	30
$4 \times 6 =$	24
$3 \times 6 =$	18
$2 \times 6 =$	12
$1 \times 6 =$	6

$12 \times 7 =$	84	$9 \times 7 =$	42
$11 \times 7 =$	77	$5 \times 7 =$	35
$10 \times 7 =$	70	$4 \times 7 =$	28
$9 \times 7 =$	63	$3 \times 7 =$	21
$8 \times 7 =$	56	$2 \times 7 =$	14
$7 \times 7 =$	49	$1 \times 7 =$	7

$12 \times 8 =$	96	$6 \times 8 =$	48
$11 \times 8 =$	88	$5 \times 8 =$	40
$10 \times 8 =$	80	$4 \times 8 =$	32
$9 \times 8 =$	72	$3 \times 8 =$	24
$8 \times 8 =$	64	$2 \times 8 =$	16
$7 \times 8 =$	56	$1 \times 8 =$	8

12 × 9 =	108
11 × 9 =	99
10 × 9 =	90
9 × 9 =	81
8 × 9 =	72
7 × 9 =	63
6 × 9 =	54
5 × 9 =	45
4 × 9 =	36
3 × 9 =	27
2 × 9 =	18
1 × 9 =	9

$12 \times 10 =$	120
$11 \times 10 =$	110
$10 \times 10 =$	100
$9 \times 10 =$	90
$8 \times 10 =$	80
$7 \times 10 =$	70
$6 \times 10 =$	60
$5 \times 10 =$	50
$4 \times 10 =$	40
$3 \times 10 =$	30
$2 \times 10 =$	20
$1 \times 10 =$	10

$11 \times 12 =$	$11 \times 11 =$	$10 \times 11 =$	$9 \times 11 =$	$8 \times 11 =$	$7 \times 11 =$
132	121	110	99	88	77
$6 \times 11 =$	$5 \times 11 =$	$4 \times 11 =$	$3 \times 11 =$	$2 \times 11 =$	$1 \times 11 =$
66	55	44	33	22	11

12 × 12 =	144	6 × 12 =
11 × 12 =	132	5 × 12 =
10 × 12 =	120	4 × 12 =
9 × 12 =	108	3 × 12 =
8 × 12 =	96	2 × 12 =
7 × 12 =	84	1 × 12 =

72	
60	
48	
36	
24	
12	

Going dotty!

Put **0** dots in each box and then finish the table.

1 × **0** =	☐							
2 × **0** =	☐	☐						
3 × **0** =	☐	☐	☐					
4 × **0** =	☐	☐	☐	☐				
5 × **0** =	☐	☐	☐	☐	☐			
6 × **0** =	☐	☐	☐	☐	☐	☐		
7 × **0** =	☐	☐	☐	☐	☐	☐	☐	
8 × **0** =	☐	☐	☐	☐	☐	☐	☐	☐
9 × **0** =	☐	☐	☐	☐	☐	☐	☐	☐
10 × **0** =	☐	☐	☐	☐	☐	☐	☐	☐
11 × **0** =	☐	☐	☐	☐	☐	☐	☐	☐
12 × **0** =	☐	☐	☐	☐	☐	☐	☐	☐

Put **1** dot in each box and then finish the table.

1 × 1 =	☐										
2 × 1 =	☐	☐									
3 × 1 =	☐	☐	☐								
4 × 1 =	☐	☐	☐	☐							
5 × 1 =	☐	☐	☐	☐	☐						
6 × 1 =	☐	☐	☐	☐	☐	☐					
7 × 1 =	☐	☐	☐	☐	☐	☐	☐				
8 × 1 =	☐	☐	☐	☐	☐	☐	☐	☐			
9 × 1 =	☐	☐	☐	☐	☐	☐	☐	☐	☐		
10 × 1 =	☐	☐	☐	☐	☐	☐	☐	☐	☐	☐	
11 × 1 =	☐	☐	☐	☐	☐	☐	☐	☐	☐	☐	☐
12 × 1 =	☐	☐	☐	☐	☐	☐	☐	☐	☐	☐	☐

Put **2** dots in each box and then finish the table.

1 × 2 =	☐										
2 × 2 =	☐	☐									
3 × 2 =	☐	☐	☐								
4 × 2 =	☐	☐	☐	☐							
5 × 2 =	☐	☐	☐	☐	☐						
6 × 2 =	☐	☐	☐	☐	☐	☐					
7 × 2 =	☐	☐	☐	☐	☐	☐	☐				
8 × 2 =	☐	☐	☐	☐	☐	☐	☐	☐			
9 × 2 =	☐	☐	☐	☐	☐	☐	☐	☐	☐		
10 × 2 =	☐	☐	☐	☐	☐	☐	☐	☐	☐	☐	
11 × 2 =	☐	☐	☐	☐	☐	☐	☐	☐	☐	☐	☐
12 × 2 =	☐	☐	☐	☐	☐	☐	☐	☐	☐	☐	☐	☐

Put **3** dots in each box and then finish the table.

1 × 3 =	☐					
2 × 3 =	☐	☐				
3 × 3 =	☐	☐	☐			
4 × 3 =	☐	☐	☐	☐		
5 × 3 =	☐	☐	☐	☐	☐	
6 × 3 =	☐	☐	☐	☐	☐	☐
7 × 3 =	☐	☐	☐	☐	☐	☐
8 × 3 =	☐	☐	☐	☐	☐	☐
9 × 3 =	☐	☐	☐	☐	☐	☐
10 × 3 =	☐	☐	☐	☐	☐	☐
11 × 3 =	☐	☐	☐	☐	☐	☐
12 × 3 =	☐	☐	☐	☐	☐	☐

Put **4** dots in each box and then finish the table.

1 × **4** =	☐										
2 × **4** =	☐	☐									
3 × **4** =	☐	☐	☐								
4 × **4** =	☐	☐	☐	☐							
5 × **4** =	☐	☐	☐	☐	☐						
6 × **4** =	☐	☐	☐	☐	☐	☐					
7 × **4** =	☐	☐	☐	☐	☐	☐	☐				
8 × **4** =	☐	☐	☐	☐	☐	☐	☐	☐			
9 × **4** =	☐	☐	☐	☐	☐	☐	☐	☐	☐		
10 × **4** =	☐	☐	☐	☐	☐	☐	☐	☐	☐	☐	
11 × **4** =	☐	☐	☐	☐	☐	☐	☐	☐	☐	☐	☐
12 × **4** =	☐	☐	☐	☐	☐	☐	☐	☐	☐	☐	☐	☐

Put **5** dots in each box and then finish the table.

1 × 5 =	
2 × 5 =	
3 × 5 =	
4 × 5 =	
5 × 5 =	
6 × 5 =	
7 × 5 =	
8 × 5 =	
9 × 5 =	
10 × 5 =	
11 × 5 =	
12 × 5 =	

Put **6** dots in each box and then finish the table.

1 × **6** =							
2 × **6** =							
3 × **6** =							
4 × **6** =							
5 × **6** =							
6 × **6** =							
7 × **6** =							
8 × **6** =							
9 × **6** =							
10 × **6** =							
11 × **6** =							
12 × **6** =							

Put **7** dots in each box and then finish the table.

1 × 7 =										☐
2 × 7 =									☐	☐
3 × 7 =								☐	☐	☐
4 × 7 =							☐	☐	☐	☐
5 × 7 =						☐	☐	☐	☐	☐
6 × 7 =					☐	☐	☐	☐	☐	☐
7 × 7 =				☐	☐	☐	☐	☐	☐	☐
8 × 7 =			☐	☐	☐	☐	☐	☐	☐	☐
9 × 7 =		☐	☐	☐	☐	☐	☐	☐	☐	☐
10 × 7 =	☐	☐	☐	☐	☐	☐	☐	☐	☐	☐
11 × 7 =	☐	☐	☐	☐	☐	☐	☐	☐	☐	☐
12 × 7 =	☐	☐	☐	☐	☐	☐	☐	☐	☐	☐

Put **8** dots in each box and then finish the table.

1											□
2										□	□
3									□	□	□
4								□	□	□	□
5							□	□	□	□	□
6						□	□	□	□	□	□
7					□	□	□	□	□	□	□
8				□	□	□	□	□	□	□	□
9			□	□	□	□	□	□	□	□	□
10		□	□	□	□	□	□	□	□	□	□
11	□	□	□	□	□	□	□	□	□	□	□
12	□	□	□	□	□	□	□	□	□	□	□

$1 \times 8 =$

$2 \times 8 =$

$3 \times 8 =$

$4 \times 8 =$

$5 \times 8 =$

$6 \times 8 =$

$7 \times 8 =$

$8 \times 8 =$

$9 \times 8 =$

$10 \times 8 =$

$11 \times 8 =$

$12 \times 8 =$

Put 9 dots in each box and then finish the table.

1 × 9 =										☐
2 × 9 =									☐	☐
3 × 9 =								☐	☐	☐
4 × 9 =							☐	☐	☐	☐
5 × 9 =						☐	☐	☐	☐	☐
6 × 9 =					☐	☐	☐	☐	☐	☐
7 × 9 =				☐	☐	☐	☐	☐	☐	☐
8 × 9 =			☐	☐	☐	☐	☐	☐	☐	☐
9 × 9 =		☐	☐	☐	☐	☐	☐	☐	☐	☐
10 × 9 =	☐	☐	☐	☐	☐	☐	☐	☐	☐	☐
11 × 9 =	☐	☐	☐	☐	☐	☐	☐	☐	☐	☐
12 × 9 =	☐	☐	☐	☐	☐	☐	☐	☐	☐	☐

Put **10** dots in each box and then finish the table.

1 × 10 =	☐										
2 × 10 =	☐	☐									
3 × 10 =	☐	☐	☐								
4 × 10 =	☐	☐	☐	☐							
5 × 10 =	☐	☐	☐	☐	☐						
6 × 10 =	☐	☐	☐	☐	☐	☐					
7 × 10 =	☐	☐	☐	☐	☐	☐	☐				
8 × 10 =	☐	☐	☐	☐	☐	☐	☐	☐			
9 × 10 =	☐	☐	☐	☐	☐	☐	☐	☐	☐		
10 × 10 =	☐	☐	☐	☐	☐	☐	☐	☐	☐	☐	
11 × 10 =	☐	☐	☐	☐	☐	☐	☐	☐	☐	☐	☐
12 × 10 =	☐	☐	☐	☐	☐	☐	☐	☐	☐	☐	☐	☐

Put 11 dots in each box and then finish the table.

1 × 11 =		
2 × 11 =		
3 × 11 =		
4 × 11 =		
5 × 11 =		
6 × 11 =		
7 × 11 =		
8 × 11 =		
9 × 11 =		
10 × 11 =		
11 × 11 =		
12 × 11 =		

Put **12** dots in each box and then finish the table.

1 × **12** =

2 × **12** =

3 × **12** =

4 × **12** =

5 × **12** =

6 × **12** =

7 × **12** =

8 × **12** =

9 × **12** =

10 × **12** =

11 × **12** =

12 × **12** =

Colour in the tables you can say without looking

Count and colour tables

Now can you do this table?

2-times table

$$0 \times 2 =$$
$$1 \times 2 =$$
$$2 \times 2 =$$
$$3 \times 2 =$$
$$4 \times 2 =$$
$$5 \times 2 =$$
$$6 \times 2 =$$
$$7 \times 2 =$$
$$8 \times 2 =$$
$$9 \times 2 =$$
$$10 \times 2 =$$
$$11 \times 2 =$$
$$12 \times 2 =$$

Count and colour in twos.
Can you see a pattern?

1	2	3	4	5	6	7	8	9	10
11	12	13	14	15	16	17	18	19	20
21	22	23	24	25	26	27	28	29	30
31	32	33	34	35	36	37	38	39	40
41	42	43	44	45	46	47	48	49	50
51	52	53	54	55	56	57	58	59	60
61	62	63	64	65	66	67	68	69	70
71	72	73	74	75	76	77	78	79	80
81	82	83	84	85	86	87	88	89	90
91	92	93	94	95	96	97	98	99	100
101	102	103	104	105	106	107	108	109	110
111	112	113	114	115	116	117	118	119	120
121	122	123	124	125	126	127	128	129	130
131	132	133	134	135	136	137	138	139	140
141	142	143	144	145	146	147	148	149	150

Now can you do this table?

3-times table

0 × 3 =

1 × 3 =

2 × 3 =

3 × 3 =

4 × 3 =

5 × 3 =

6 × 3 =

7 × 3 =

8 × 3 =

9 × 3 =

10 × 3 =

11 × 3 =

12 × 3 =

Count and colour in threes. Can you see a pattern?

1	2	3	4	5	6	7	8	9	10
11	12	13	14	15	16	17	18	19	20
21	22	23	24	25	26	27	28	29	30
31	32	33	34	35	36	37	38	39	40
41	42	43	44	45	46	47	48	49	50
51	52	53	54	55	56	57	58	59	60
61	62	63	64	65	66	67	68	69	70
71	72	73	74	75	76	77	78	79	80
81	82	83	84	85	86	87	88	89	90
91	92	93	94	95	96	97	98	99	100
101	102	103	104	105	106	107	108	109	110
111	112	113	114	115	116	117	118	119	120
121	122	123	124	125	126	127	128	129	130
131	132	133	134	135	136	137	138	139	140
141	142	143	144	145	146	147	148	149	150

Now can you do this table?

4-times table

0 × 4 =

1 × 4 =

2 × 4 =

3 × 4 =

4 × 4 =

5 × 4 =

6 × 4 =

7 × 4 =

8 × 4 =

9 × 4 =

10 × 4 =

11 × 4 =

12 × 4 =

Count and colour in fours. Can you see a pattern?

1	2	3	4	5	6	7	8	9	10
11	12	13	14	15	16	17	18	19	20
21	22	23	24	25	26	27	28	29	30
31	32	33	34	35	36	37	38	39	40
41	42	43	44	45	46	47	48	49	50
51	52	53	54	55	56	57	58	59	60
61	62	63	64	65	66	67	68	69	70
71	72	73	74	75	76	77	78	79	80
81	82	83	84	85	86	87	88	89	90
91	92	93	94	95	96	97	98	99	100
101	102	103	104	105	106	107	108	109	110
111	112	113	114	115	116	117	118	119	120
121	122	123	124	125	126	127	128	129	130
131	132	133	134	135	136	137	138	139	140
141	142	143	144	145	146	147	148	149	150

Now can you do this table?

5-times table

0 × **5**	=	
1 × **5**	=	
2 × **5**	=	
3 × **5**	=	
4 × **5**	=	
5 × **5**	=	
6 × **5**	=	
7 × **5**	=	
8 × **5**	=	
9 × **5**	=	
10 × **5**	=	
11 × **5**	=	
12 × **5**	=	

Count and colour in fives.
Can you see a pattern?

1	2	3	4	5	6	7	8	9	10
11	12	13	14	15	16	17	18	19	20
21	22	23	24	25	26	27	28	29	30
31	32	33	34	35	36	37	38	39	40
41	42	43	44	45	46	47	48	49	50
51	52	53	54	55	56	57	58	59	60
61	62	63	64	65	66	67	68	69	70
71	72	73	74	75	76	77	78	79	80
81	82	83	84	85	86	87	88	89	90
91	92	93	94	95	96	97	98	99	100
101	102	103	104	105	106	107	108	109	110
111	112	113	114	115	116	117	118	119	120
121	122	123	124	125	126	127	128	129	130
131	132	133	134	135	136	137	138	139	140
141	142	143	144	145	146	147	148	149	150

Now can you do this table?

6-times table

0 × **6** =	
1 × **6** =	
2 × **6** =	
3 × **6** =	
4 × **6** =	
5 × **6** =	
6 × **6** =	
7 × **6** =	
8 × **6** =	
9 × **6** =	
10 × **6** =	
11 × **6** =	
12 × **6** =	

Count and colour in sixes.
Can you see a pattern?

1	2	3	4	5	6	7	8	9	10
11	12	13	14	15	16	17	18	19	20
21	22	23	24	25	26	27	28	29	30
31	32	33	34	35	36	37	38	39	40
41	42	43	44	45	46	47	48	49	50
51	52	53	54	55	56	57	58	59	60
61	62	63	64	65	66	67	68	69	70
71	72	73	74	75	76	77	78	79	80
81	82	83	84	85	86	87	88	89	90
91	92	93	94	95	96	97	98	99	100
101	102	103	104	105	106	107	108	109	110
111	112	113	114	115	116	117	118	119	120
121	122	123	124	125	126	127	128	129	130
131	132	133	134	135	136	137	138	139	140
141	142	143	144	145	146	147	148	149	150

Count and colour in sevens. Can you see a pattern?

1	2	3	4	5	6	7	8	9	10
11	12	13	14	15	16	17	18	19	20
21	22	23	24	25	26	27	28	29	30
31	32	33	34	35	36	37	38	39	40
41	42	43	44	45	46	47	48	49	50
51	52	53	54	55	56	57	58	59	60
61	62	63	64	65	66	67	68	69	70
71	72	73	74	75	76	77	78	79	80
81	82	83	84	85	86	87	88	89	90
91	92	93	94	95	96	97	98	99	100
101	102	103	104	105	106	107	108	109	110
111	112	113	114	115	116	117	118	119	120
121	122	123	124	125	126	127	128	129	130
131	132	133	134	135	136	137	138	139	140
141	142	143	144	145	146	147	148	149	150

Now can you do this table?

7-times table

$0 \times 7 =$

$1 \times 7 =$

$2 \times 7 =$

$3 \times 7 =$

$4 \times 7 =$

$5 \times 7 =$

$6 \times 7 =$

$7 \times 7 =$

$8 \times 7 =$

$9 \times 7 =$

$10 \times 7 =$

$11 \times 7 =$

$12 \times 7 =$

Now can you do this table?

8-times table

0 × **8** =	
1 × **8** =	
2 × **8** =	
3 × **8** =	
4 × **8** =	
5 × **8** =	
6 × **8** =	
7 × **8** =	
8 × **8** =	
9 × **8** =	
10 × **8** =	
11 × **8** =	
12 × **8** =	

Count and colour in eights.
Can you see a pattern?

1	2	3	4	5	6	7	8	9	10
11	12	13	14	15	16	17	18	19	20
21	22	23	24	25	26	27	28	29	30
31	32	33	34	35	36	37	38	39	40
41	42	43	44	45	46	47	48	49	50
51	52	53	54	55	56	57	58	59	60
61	62	63	64	65	66	67	68	69	70
71	72	73	74	75	76	77	78	79	80
81	82	83	84	85	86	87	88	89	90
91	92	93	94	95	96	97	98	99	100
101	102	103	104	105	106	107	108	109	110
111	112	113	114	115	116	117	118	119	120
121	122	123	124	125	126	127	128	129	130
131	132	133	134	135	136	137	138	139	140
141	142	143	144	145	146	147	148	149	150

Now can you do this table?

9-times table

0	×	**9**	=	
1	×	**9**	=	
2	×	**9**	=	
3	×	**9**	=	
4	×	**9**	=	
5	×	**9**	=	
6	×	**9**	=	
7	×	**9**	=	
8	×	**9**	=	
9	×	**9**	=	
10	×	**9**	=	
11	×	**9**	=	
12	×	**9**	=	

Count and colour in nines.
Can you see a pattern?

1	2	3	4	5	6	7	8	9	10
11	12	13	14	15	16	17	18	19	20
21	22	23	24	25	26	27	28	29	30
31	32	33	34	35	36	37	38	39	40
41	42	43	44	45	46	47	48	49	50
51	52	53	54	55	56	57	58	59	60
61	62	63	64	65	66	67	68	69	70
71	72	73	74	75	76	77	78	79	80
81	82	83	84	85	86	87	88	89	90
91	92	93	94	95	96	97	98	99	100
101	102	103	104	105	106	107	108	109	110
111	112	113	114	115	116	117	118	119	120
121	122	123	124	125	126	127	128	129	130
131	132	133	134	135	136	137	138	139	140
141	142	143	144	145	146	147	148	149	150

Now can you do this table?

10-times table

$$0 \times 10 =$$

$$1 \times 10 =$$

$$2 \times 10 =$$

$$3 \times 10 =$$

$$4 \times 10 =$$

$$5 \times 10 =$$

$$6 \times 10 =$$

$$7 \times 10 =$$

$$8 \times 10 =$$

$$9 \times 10 =$$

$$10 \times 10 =$$

$$11 \times 10 =$$

$$12 \times 10 =$$

Count and colour in tens. Can you see a pattern?

1	2	3	4	5	6	7	8	9	10
11	12	13	14	15	16	17	18	19	20
21	22	23	24	25	26	27	28	29	30
31	32	33	34	35	36	37	38	39	40
41	42	43	44	45	46	47	48	49	50
51	52	53	54	55	56	57	58	59	60
61	62	63	64	65	66	67	68	69	70
71	72	73	74	75	76	77	78	79	80
81	82	83	84	85	86	87	88	89	90
91	92	93	94	95	96	97	98	99	100
101	102	103	104	105	106	107	108	109	110
111	112	113	114	115	116	117	118	119	120
121	122	123	124	125	126	127	128	129	130
131	132	133	134	135	136	137	138	139	140
141	142	143	144	145	146	147	148	149	150

Now can you do this table?

11-times table

0 × 11 =		
1 × 11 =		
2 × 11 =		
3 × 11 =		
4 × 11 =		
5 × 11 =		
6 × 11 =		
7 × 11 =		
8 × 11 =		
9 × 11 =		
10 × 11 =		
11 × 11 =		
12 × 11 =		

Count and colour in elevens. Can you see a pattern?

1	2	3	4	5	6	7	8	9	10
11	12	13	14	15	16	17	18	19	20
21	22	23	24	25	26	27	28	29	30
31	32	33	34	35	36	37	38	39	40
41	42	43	44	45	46	47	48	49	50
51	52	53	54	55	56	57	58	59	60
61	62	63	64	65	66	67	68	69	70
71	72	73	74	75	76	77	78	79	80
81	82	83	84	85	86	87	88	89	90
91	92	93	94	95	96	97	98	99	100
101	102	103	104	105	106	107	108	109	110
111	112	113	114	115	116	117	118	119	120
121	122	123	124	125	126	127	128	129	130
131	132	133	134	135	136	137	138	139	140
141	142	143	144	145	146	147	148	149	150

Now can you do this table?

12-times table

0 × 12 =

1 × 12 =

2 × 12 =

3 × 12 =

4 × 12 =

5 × 12 =

6 × 12 =

7 × 12 =

8 × 12 =

9 × 12 =

10 × 12 =

11 × 12 =

12 × 12 =

Count and colour in twelves. Can you see a pattern?

1	2	3	4	5	6	7	8	9	10
11	12	13	14	15	16	17	18	19	20
21	22	23	24	25	26	27	28	29	30
31	32	33	34	35	36	37	38	39	40
41	42	43	44	45	46	47	48	49	50
51	52	53	54	55	56	57	58	59	60
61	62	63	64	65	66	67	68	69	70
71	72	73	74	75	76	77	78	79	80
81	82	83	84	85	86	87	88	89	90
91	92	93	94	95	96	97	98	99	100
101	102	103	104	105	106	107	108	109	110
111	112	113	114	115	116	117	118	119	120
121	122	123	124	125	126	127	128	129	130
131	132	133	134	135	136	137	138	139	140
141	142	143	144	145	146	147	148	149	150

CERTIFICATE
I can say my

1 × table
2 × table
3 × table

1 2 3

1-times table

0 × 1 =
1 × 1 =
2 × 1 =
3 × 1 =
4 × 1 =
5 × 1 =
6 × 1 =
7 × 1 =
8 × 1 =
9 × 1 =
10 × 1 =
11 × 1 =
12 × 1 =

You write the [1]-times table

2-times table

0 × 2 =
1 × 2 =
2 × 2 =
3 × 2 =
4 × 2 =
5 × 2 =
6 × 2 =
7 × 2 =
8 × 2 =
9 × 2 =
10 × 2 =
11 × 2 =
12 × 2 =

You write the [3]-times table

3-times table

0 × 3 =
1 × 3 =
2 × 3 =
3 × 3 =
4 × 3 =
5 × 3 =
6 × 3 =
7 × 3 =
8 × 3 =
9 × 3 =
10 × 3 =
11 × 3 =
12 × 3 =

You write the [2]-times table

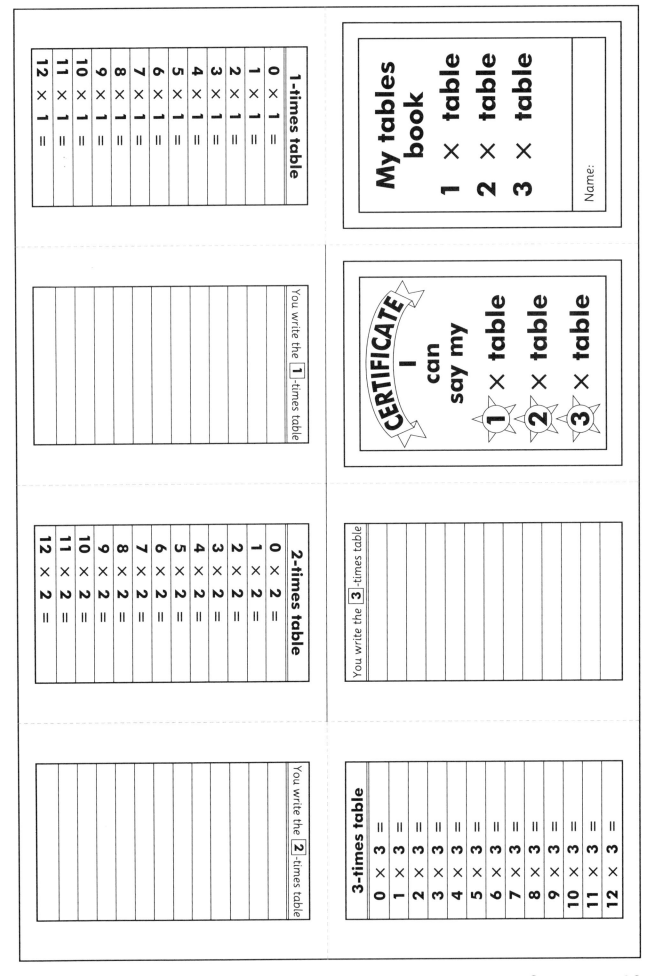

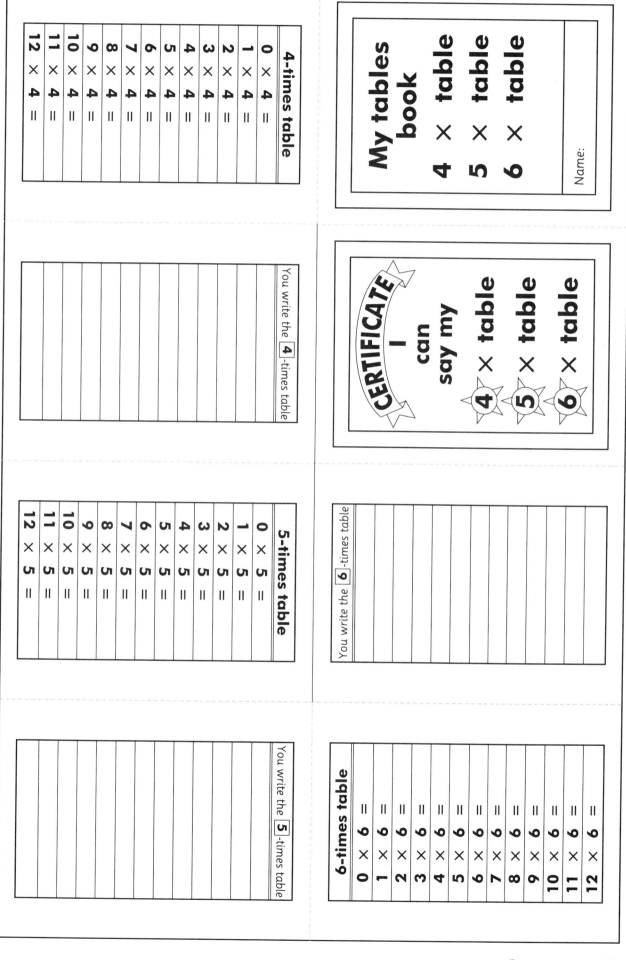

4-times table

0 × 4 =
1 × 4 =
2 × 4 =
3 × 4 =
4 × 4 =
5 × 4 =
6 × 4 =
7 × 4 =
8 × 4 =
9 × 4 =
10 × 4 =
11 × 4 =
12 × 4 =

My tables book

4 × table
5 × table
6 × table

Name:

You write the **4** -times table

CERTIFICATE
I can say my
4 × table
5 × table
6 × table

5-times table

0 × 5 =
1 × 5 =
2 × 5 =
3 × 5 =
4 × 5 =
5 × 5 =
6 × 5 =
7 × 5 =
8 × 5 =
9 × 5 =
10 × 5 =
11 × 5 =
12 × 5 =

You write the **6** -times table

You write the **5** -times table

6-times table

0 × 6 =
1 × 6 =
2 × 6 =
3 × 6 =
4 × 6 =
5 × 6 =
6 × 6 =
7 × 6 =
8 × 6 =
9 × 6 =
10 × 6 =
11 × 6 =
12 × 6 =

Copymaster 49

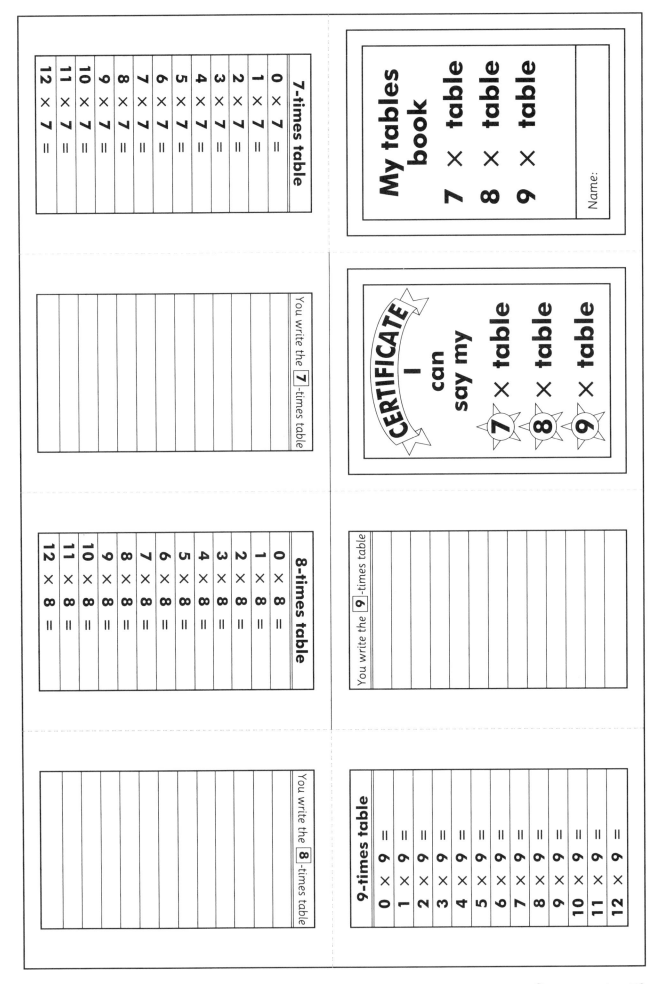

My tables book

7 × table
8 × table
9 × table

Name:

CERTIFICATE
I can say my
7 × table
8 × table
9 × table

7 8 9

7-times table

| 0 × 7 = |
| 1 × 7 = |
| 2 × 7 = |
| 3 × 7 = |
| 4 × 7 = |
| 5 × 7 = |
| 6 × 7 = |
| 7 × 7 = |
| 8 × 7 = |
| 9 × 7 = |
| 10 × 7 = |
| 11 × 7 = |
| 12 × 7 = |

You write the **7**-times table

8-times table

| 0 × 8 = |
| 1 × 8 = |
| 2 × 8 = |
| 3 × 8 = |
| 4 × 8 = |
| 5 × 8 = |
| 6 × 8 = |
| 7 × 8 = |
| 8 × 8 = |
| 9 × 8 = |
| 10 × 8 = |
| 11 × 8 = |
| 12 × 8 = |

You write the **9**-times table

You write the **8**-times table

9-times table

| 0 × 9 = |
| 1 × 9 = |
| 2 × 9 = |
| 3 × 9 = |
| 4 × 9 = |
| 5 × 9 = |
| 6 × 9 = |
| 7 × 9 = |
| 8 × 9 = |
| 9 × 9 = |
| 10 × 9 = |
| 11 × 9 = |
| 12 × 9 = |

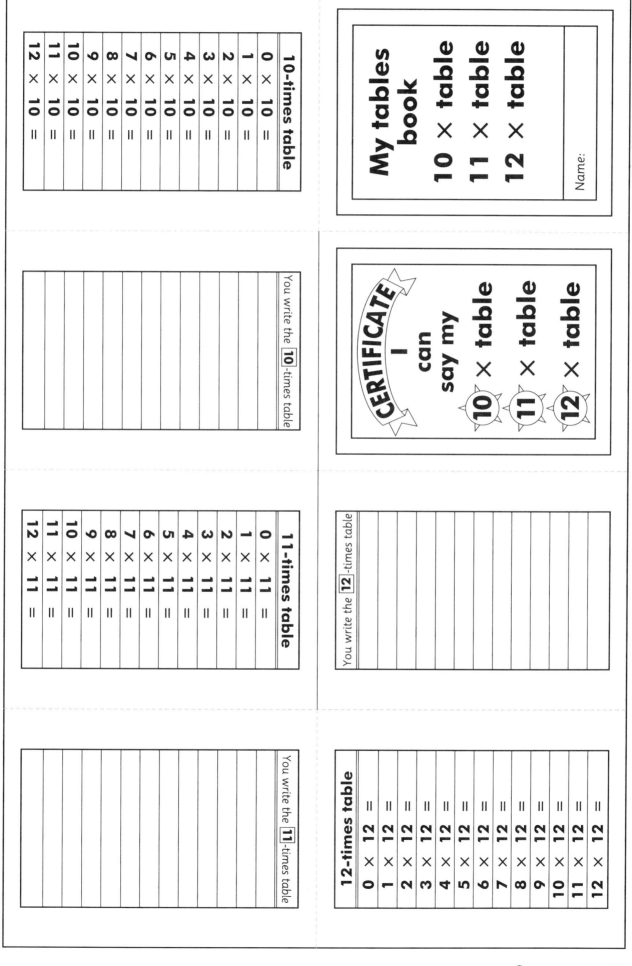

My tables book

10 × table
11 × table
12 × table

Name:

CERTIFICATE
I can say my

10 × table
11 × table
12 × table

10   11   12

10-times table

0 × 10 =		
1 × 10 =		
2 × 10 =		
3 × 10 =		
4 × 10 =		
5 × 10 =		
6 × 10 =		
7 × 10 =		
8 × 10 =		
9 × 10 =		
10 × 10 =		
11 × 10 =		
12 × 10 =		

You write the **10**-times table

You write the **12**-times table

11-times table

0 × 11 =		
1 × 11 =		
2 × 11 =		
3 × 11 =		
4 × 11 =		
5 × 11 =		
6 × 11 =		
7 × 11 =		
8 × 11 =		
9 × 11 =		
10 × 11 =		
11 × 11 =		
12 × 11 =		

You write the **11**-times table

12-times table

0 × 12 =		
1 × 12 =		
2 × 12 =		
3 × 12 =		
4 × 12 =		
5 × 12 =		
6 × 12 =		
7 × 12 =		
8 × 12 =		
9 × 12 =		
10 × 12 =		
11 × 12 =		
12 × 12 =		

Tables mazes

All of the mazes look the same but they are all different. See if you can get through!

1-times table maze

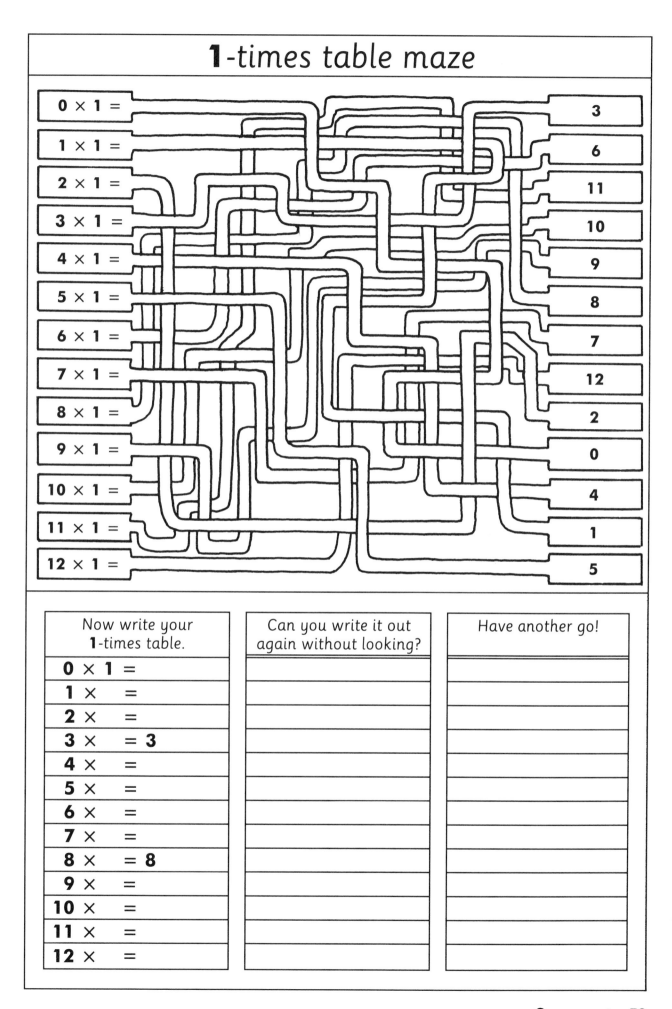

0 × 1 =		3
1 × 1 =		6
2 × 1 =		11
3 × 1 =		10
4 × 1 =		9
5 × 1 =		8
6 × 1 =		7
7 × 1 =		12
8 × 1 =		2
9 × 1 =		0
10 × 1 =		4
11 × 1 =		1
12 × 1 =		5

Now write your **1**-times table.	Can you write it out again without looking?	Have another go!
0 × **1** =		
1 × =		
2 × =		
3 × = 3		
4 × =		
5 × =		
6 × =		
7 × =		
8 × = 8		
9 × =		
10 × =		
11 × =		
12 × =		

2-times table maze

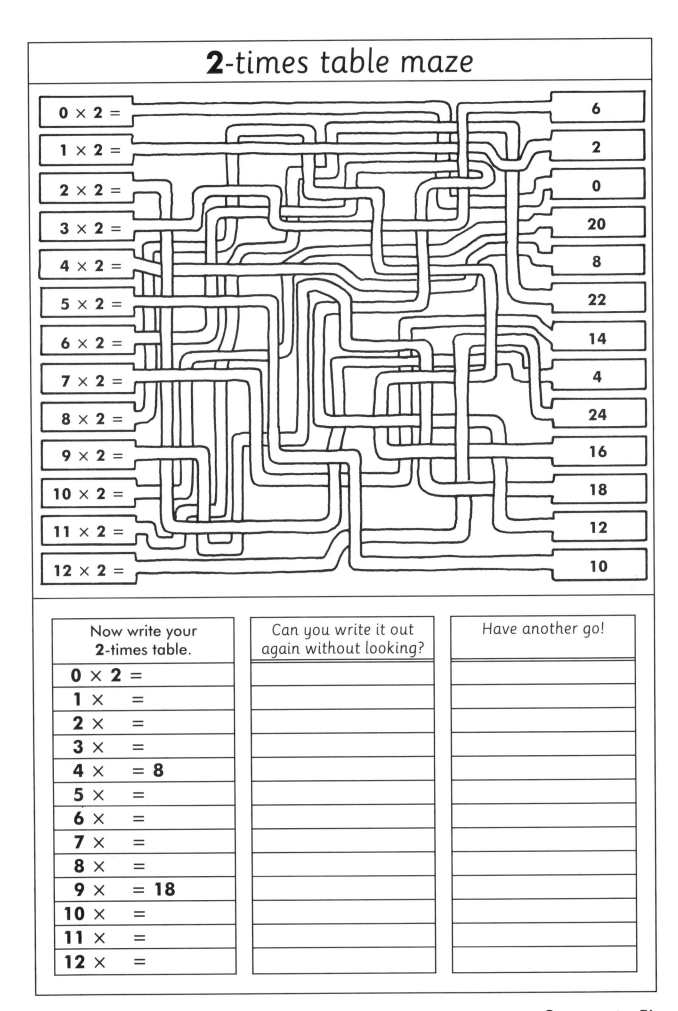

0 × 2 =		6
1 × 2 =		2
2 × 2 =		0
3 × 2 =		20
4 × 2 =		8
5 × 2 =		22
6 × 2 =		14
7 × 2 =		4
8 × 2 =		24
9 × 2 =		16
10 × 2 =		18
11 × 2 =		12
12 × 2 =		10

Now write your **2**-times table.	Can you write it out again without looking?	Have another go!
0 × 2 =		
1 × =		
2 × =		
3 × =		
4 × = 8		
5 × =		
6 × =		
7 × =		
8 × =		
9 × = 18		
10 × =		
11 × =		
12 × =		

3-times table maze

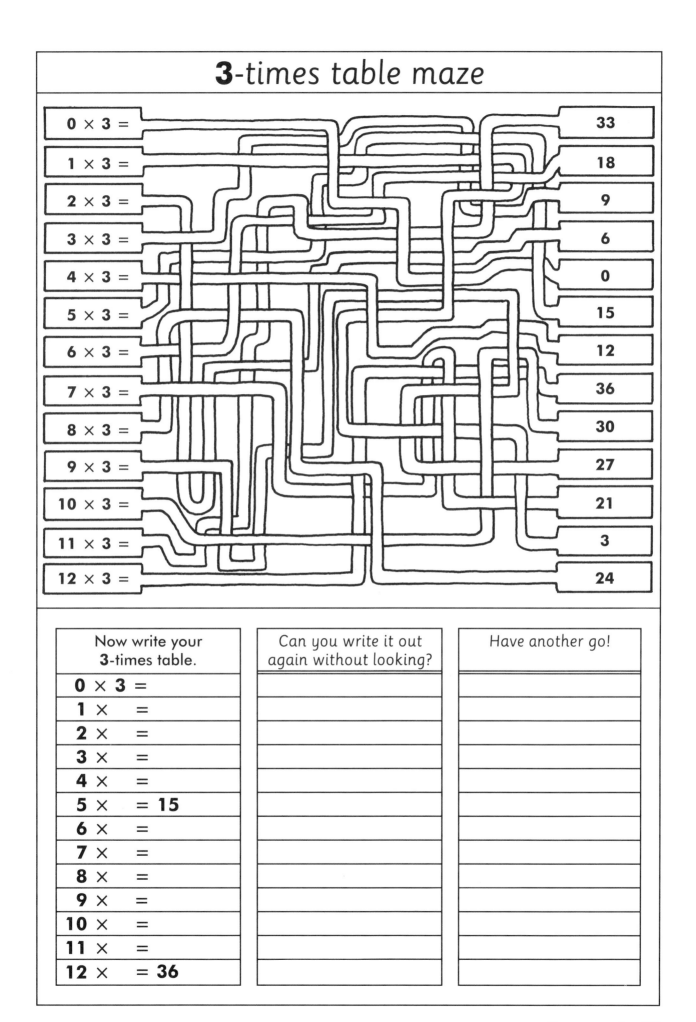

0 × 3 =		33
1 × 3 =		18
2 × 3 =		9
3 × 3 =		6
4 × 3 =		0
5 × 3 =		15
6 × 3 =		12
7 × 3 =		36
8 × 3 =		30
9 × 3 =		27
10 × 3 =		21
11 × 3 =		3
12 × 3 =		24

Now write your **3**-times table.	Can you write it out again without looking?	Have another go!
0 × 3 =		
1 × =		
2 × =		
3 × =		
4 × =		
5 × = 15		
6 × =		
7 × =		
8 × =		
9 × =		
10 × =		
11 × =		
12 × = 36		

4-times table maze

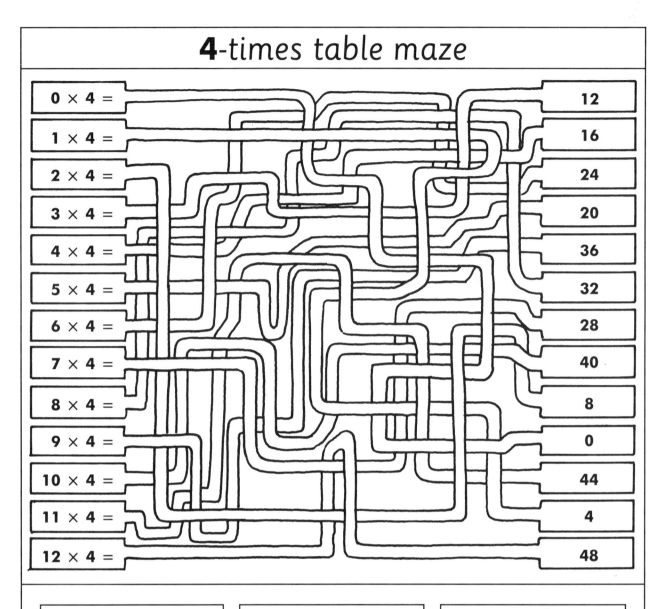

0 × 4 =		12
1 × 4 =		16
2 × 4 =		24
3 × 4 =		20
4 × 4 =		36
5 × 4 =		32
6 × 4 =		28
7 × 4 =		40
8 × 4 =		8
9 × 4 =		0
10 × 4 =		44
11 × 4 =		4
12 × 4 =		48

Now write your **4**-times table.	Can you write it out again without looking?	Have another go!
0 × 4 =		
1 × = **4**		
2 × =		
3 × =		
4 × =		
5 × =		
6 × =		
7 × = **28**		
8 × =		
9 × =		
10 × =		
11 × =		
12 × =		

5-times table maze

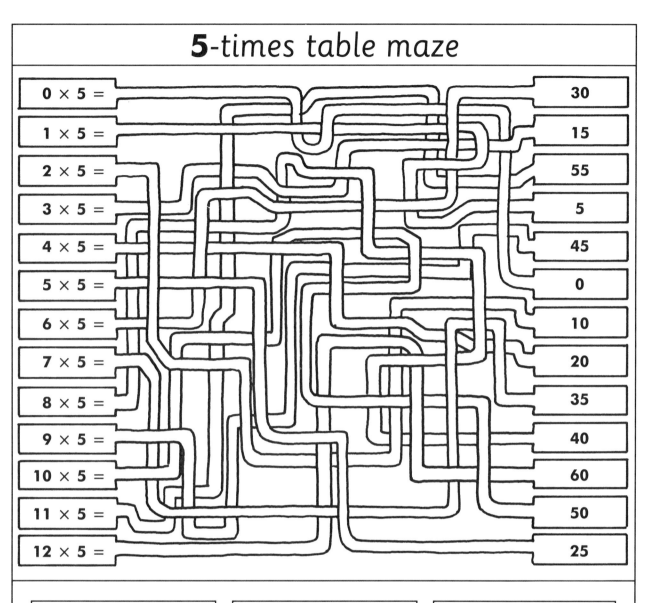

0 × 5 =		30
1 × 5 =		15
2 × 5 =		55
3 × 5 =		5
4 × 5 =		45
5 × 5 =		0
6 × 5 =		10
7 × 5 =		20
8 × 5 =		35
9 × 5 =		40
10 × 5 =		60
11 × 5 =		50
12 × 5 =		25

Now write your 5-times table.	Can you write it out again without looking?	Have another go!
0 × 5 =		
1 × =		
2 × =		
3 × =		
4 × =		
5 × = 25		
6 × =		
7 × =		
8 × = 40		
9 × =		
10 × =		
11 × =		
12 × =		

6-times table maze

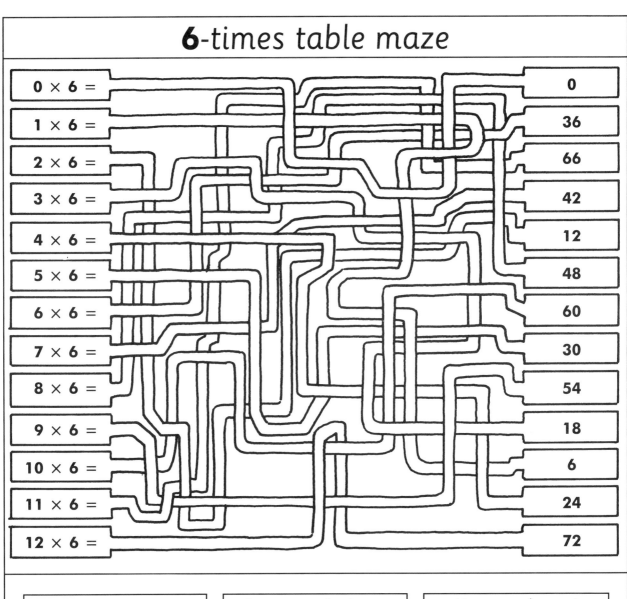

0 × 6 =		0
1 × 6 =		36
2 × 6 =		66
3 × 6 =		42
4 × 6 =		12
5 × 6 =		48
6 × 6 =		60
7 × 6 =		30
8 × 6 =		54
9 × 6 =		18
10 × 6 =		6
11 × 6 =		24
12 × 6 =		72

Now write your **6**-times table.	Can you write it out again without looking?	Have another go!
0 × 6 =		
1 × =		
2 × =		
3 × = 18		
4 × =		
5 × =		
6 × =		
7 × =		
8 × =		
9 × =		
10 × = 60		
11 × =		
12 × =		

7-times table maze

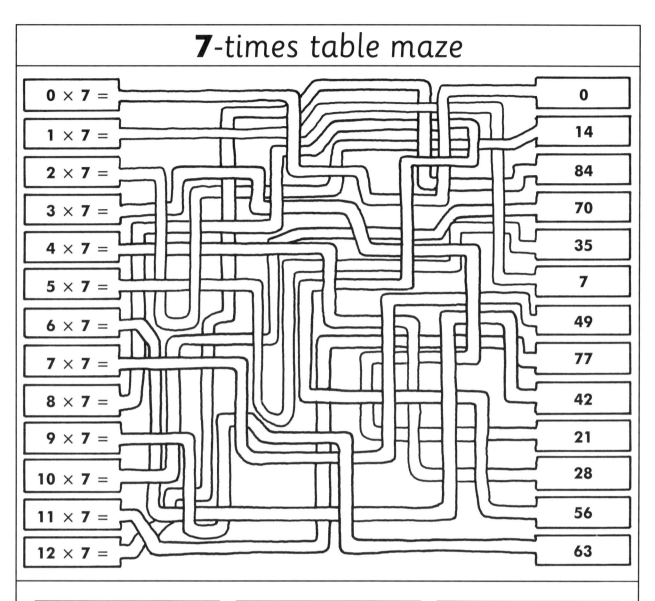

0 × 7 =		0
1 × 7 =		14
2 × 7 =		84
3 × 7 =		70
4 × 7 =		35
5 × 7 =		7
6 × 7 =		49
7 × 7 =		77
8 × 7 =		42
9 × 7 =		21
10 × 7 =		28
11 × 7 =		56
12 × 7 =		63

Now write your **7**-times table.	Can you write it out again without looking?	Have another go!
0 × 7 =		
1 × =		
2 × =		
3 × =		
4 × = 28		
5 × =		
6 × =		
7 × =		
8 × =		
9 × =		
10 × =		
11 × = 77		
12 × =		

8-times table maze

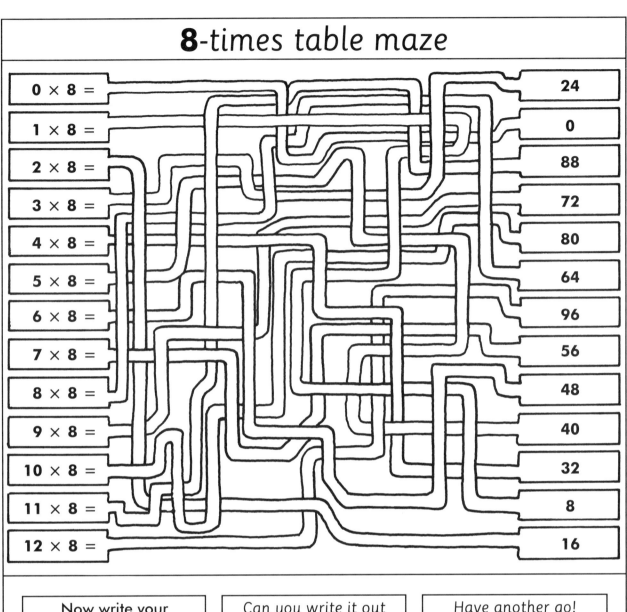

0 × 8 =		24
1 × 8 =		0
2 × 8 =		88
3 × 8 =		72
4 × 8 =		80
5 × 8 =		64
6 × 8 =		96
7 × 8 =		56
8 × 8 =		48
9 × 8 =		40
10 × 8 =		32
11 × 8 =		8
12 × 8 =		16

Now write your 8-times table.	Can you write it out again without looking?	Have another go!
0 × 8 =		
1 × =		
2 × = 16		
3 × =		
4 × =		
5 × =		
6 × =		
7 × = 56		
8 × =		
9 × =		
10 × =		
11 × =		
12 × =		

9-times table maze

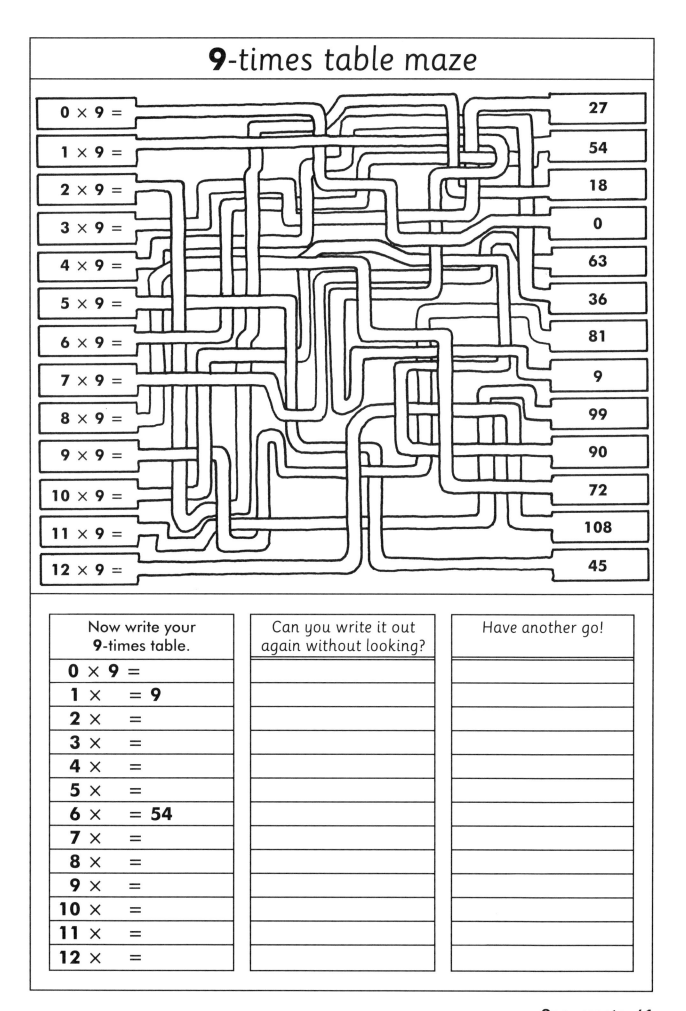

0 × 9 =		27
1 × 9 =		54
2 × 9 =		18
3 × 9 =		0
4 × 9 =		63
5 × 9 =		36
6 × 9 =		81
7 × 9 =		9
8 × 9 =		99
9 × 9 =		90
10 × 9 =		72
11 × 9 =		108
12 × 9 =		45

Now write your 9-times table.	Can you write it out again without looking?	Have another go!
0 × 9 =		
1 × = 9		
2 × =		
3 × =		
4 × =		
5 × =		
6 × = 54		
7 × =		
8 × =		
9 × =		
10 × =		
11 × =		
12 × =		

10-times table maze

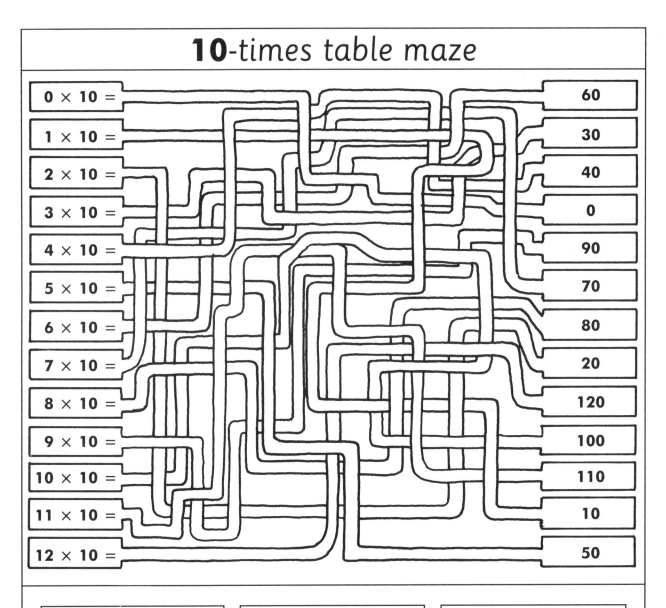

0 × 10 =		60
1 × 10 =		30
2 × 10 =		40
3 × 10 =		0
4 × 10 =		90
5 × 10 =		70
6 × 10 =		80
7 × 10 =		20
8 × 10 =		120
9 × 10 =		100
10 × 10 =		110
11 × 10 =		10
12 × 10 =		50

Now write your 10-times table.	Can you write it out again without looking?	Have another go!
0 × 10 =		
1 × = 10		
2 × =		
3 × =		
4 × =		
5 × =		
6 × =		
7 × =		
8 × =		
9 × =		
10 × = 100		
11 × =		
12 × =		

11-times table maze

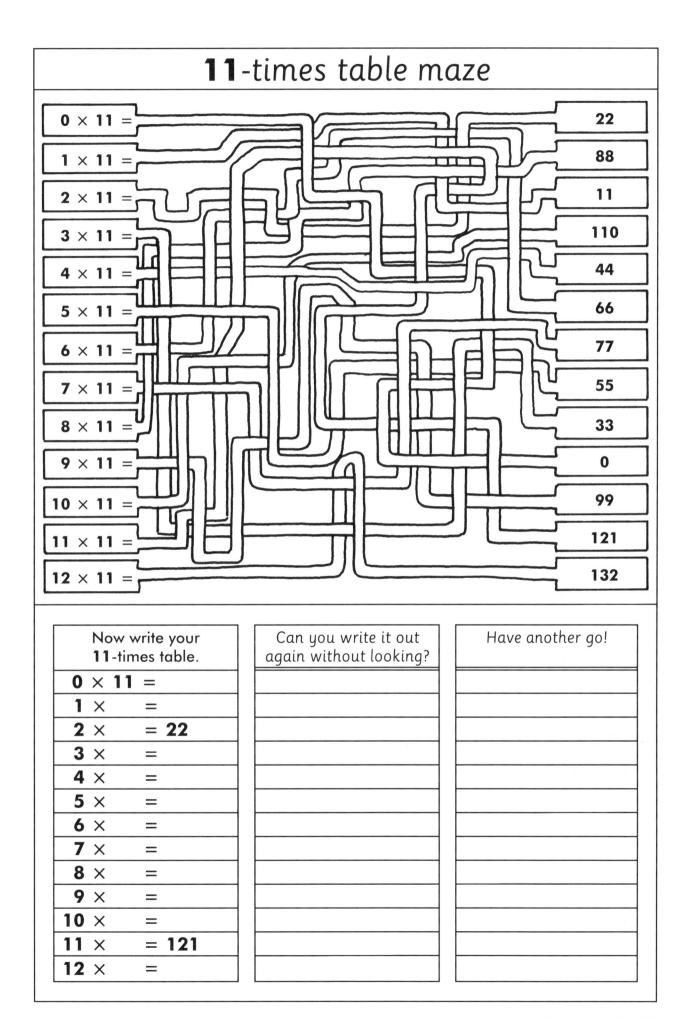

0 × 11 =		22
1 × 11 =		88
2 × 11 =		11
3 × 11 =		110
4 × 11 =		44
5 × 11 =		66
6 × 11 =		77
7 × 11 =		55
8 × 11 =		33
9 × 11 =		0
10 × 11 =		99
11 × 11 =		121
12 × 11 =		132

Now write your 11-times table.	Can you write it out again without looking?	Have another go!
0 × 11 =		
1 × =		
2 × = 22		
3 × =		
4 × =		
5 × =		
6 × =		
7 × =		
8 × =		
9 × =		
10 × =		
11 × = 121		
12 × =		

12-times table maze

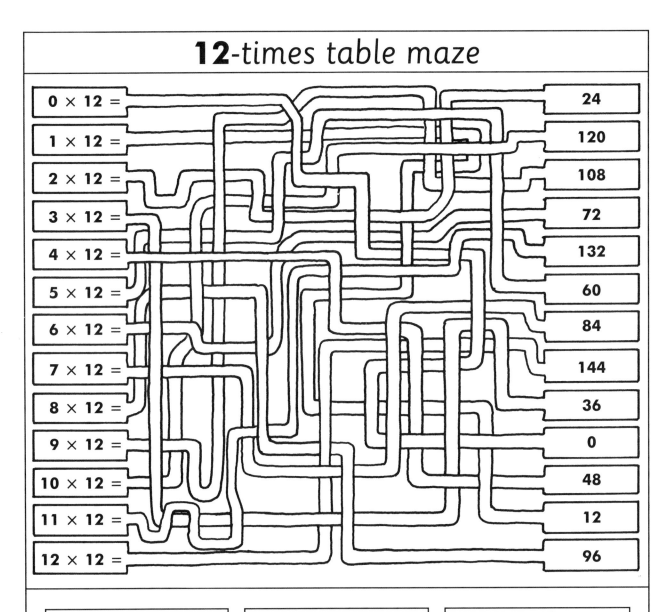

0 × 12 =		24
1 × 12 =		120
2 × 12 =		108
3 × 12 =		72
4 × 12 =		132
5 × 12 =		60
6 × 12 =		84
7 × 12 =		144
8 × 12 =		36
9 × 12 =		0
10 × 12 =		48
11 × 12 =		12
12 × 12 =		96

Now write your 12-times table.	Can you write it out again without looking?	Have another go!
0 × 12 =		
1 × =		
2 × = 24		
3 × =		
4 × =		
5 × =		
6 × =		
7 × =		
8 × = 96		
9 × =		
10 × =		
11 × =		
12 × =		

Make your own ☐-times table maze

0 × ☐ = ☐
1 × ☐ = ☐
2 × ☐ = ☐
3 × ☐ = ☐
4 × ☐ = ☐
5 × ☐ = ☐
6 × ☐ = ☐
7 × ☐ = ☐
8 × ☐ = ☐
9 × ☐ = ☐
10 × ☐ = ☐
11 × ☐ = ☐
12 × ☐ = ☐

Now write your ☐ times table.	Can you write it out again without looking?	Have another go!
0 × ☐ =		
1 × ☐ =		
2 × ☐ =		
3 × ☐ =		
4 × ☐ =		
5 × ☐ =		
6 × ☐ =		
7 × ☐ =		
8 × ☐ =		
9 × ☐ =		
10 × ☐ =		
11 × ☐ =		
12 × ☐ =		

HOW WELL DID YOU DO?

Only colour in a box if you got all of a table right.

When you have coloured in all five boxes for any of the tables, you can give yourself a certificate.

0-times table				
1-times table				
2-times table				
3-times table				
4-times table				
5-times table				
6-times table				
7-times table				
8-times table				
9-times table				
10-times table				
11-times table				
12-times table				

Hard Tables Test Book

The numbers are mixed up for you!

Test A		0-times table

0-times table

1 × 0 =	
10 × 0 =	
3 × 0 =	
7 × 0 =	
0 × 0 =	
9 × 0 =	
2 × 0 =	
11 × 0 =	
5 × 0 =	
12 × 0 =	
8 × 0 =	
6 × 0 =	
4 × 0 =	

SCORE

Best of luck!

13

Check your answers. Learn the ones you got wrong and try again. If you got all 13 right, colour in a box on the chart.

Test B		0-times table

0-times table

7 × 0 =	
2 × 0 =	
11 × 0 =	
9 × 0 =	
5 × 0 =	
8 × 0 =	
12 × 0 =	
6 × 0 =	
4 × 0 =	
0 × 0 =	
3 × 0 =	
1 × 0 =	
10 × 0 =	

SCORE

Best of luck!

13

Check your answers. Learn the ones you got wrong and try again. If you got all 13 right, colour in a box on the chart.

Test A

1-times table

1 × 1	=		
10 × 1	=		
3 × 1	=		
7 × 1	=		
0 × 1	=		
9 × 1	=		
2 × 1	=		
11 × 1	=		
5 × 1	=		
12 × 1	=		
8 × 1	=		
6 × 1	=		
4 × 1	=		

SCORE

Best of luck!

▭/13

Check your answers. Learn the ones you got wrong and try again. If you got all 13 right, colour in a box on the chart.

Test B

1-times table

7 × 1	=		
2 × 1	=		
11 × 1	=		
9 × 1	=		
5 × 1	=		
8 × 1	=		
12 × 1	=		
6 × 1	=		
4 × 1	=		
0 × 1	=		
3 × 1	=		
1 × 1	=		
10 × 1	=		

SCORE

Best of luck!

▭/13

Check your answers. Learn the ones you got wrong and try again. If you got all 13 right, colour in a box on the chart.

Test A

2-times table

1	×	2 =	
10	×	2 =	
3	×	2 =	
7	×	2 =	
0	×	2 =	
9	×	2 =	
2	×	2 =	
11	×	2 =	
5	×	2 =	
12	×	2 =	
8	×	2 =	
6	×	2 =	
4	×	2 =	

Best of luck!

SCORE

□/13

Check your answers. Learn the ones you got wrong and try again. If you got all 13 right, colour in a box on the chart.

Test B

2-times table

7	×	2 =	
2	×	2 =	
11	×	2 =	
9	×	2 =	
5	×	2 =	
8	×	2 =	
12	×	2 =	
6	×	2 =	
4	×	2 =	
0	×	2 =	
3	×	2 =	
1	×	2 =	
10	×	2 =	

Best of luck!

SCORE

□/13

Check your answers. Learn the ones you got wrong and try again. If you got all 13 right, colour in a box on the chart.

Test A

3-times table

1 × 3 =		
10 × 3 =		
3 × 3 =		
7 × 3 =		
0 × 3 =		
9 × 3 =		
2 × 3 =		
11 × 3 =		
5 × 3 =		
12 × 3 =		
8 × 3 =		
6 × 3 =		
4 × 3 =		

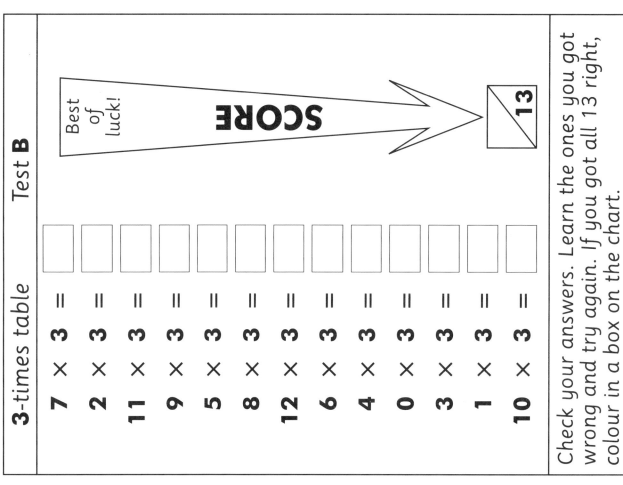

SCORE

Best of luck!

13

Check your answers. Learn the ones you got wrong and try again. If you got all 13 right, colour in a box on the chart.

Test B

3-times table

7 × 3 =		
2 × 3 =		
11 × 3 =		
9 × 3 =		
5 × 3 =		
8 × 3 =		
12 × 3 =		
6 × 3 =		
4 × 3 =		
0 × 3 =		
3 × 3 =		
1 × 3 =		
10 × 3 =		

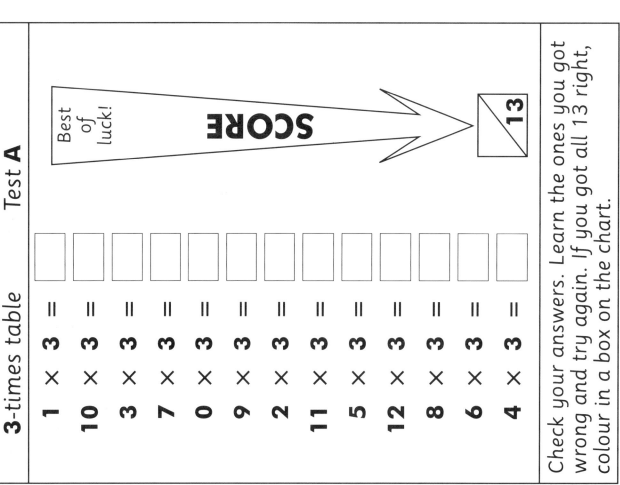

SCORE

Best of luck!

13

Check your answers. Learn the ones you got wrong and try again. If you got all 13 right, colour in a box on the chart.

Test A

4-times table

1 × 4 =		
10 × 4 =		
3 × 4 =		
7 × 4 =		
0 × 4 =		
9 × 4 =		
2 × 4 =		
11 × 4 =		
5 × 4 =		
12 × 4 =		
8 × 4 =		
6 × 4 =		
4 × 4 =		

Best of luck!

SCORE

□/13

Check your answers. Learn the ones you got wrong and try again. If you got all 13 right, colour in a box on the chart.

Test B

4-times table

7 × 4 =		
2 × 4 =		
11 × 4 =		
9 × 4 =		
5 × 4 =		
8 × 4 =		
12 × 4 =		
6 × 4 =		
4 × 4 =		
0 × 4 =		
3 × 4 =		
1 × 4 =		
10 × 4 =		

Best of luck!

SCORE

□/13

Check your answers. Learn the ones you got wrong and try again. If you got all 13 right, colour in a box on the chart.

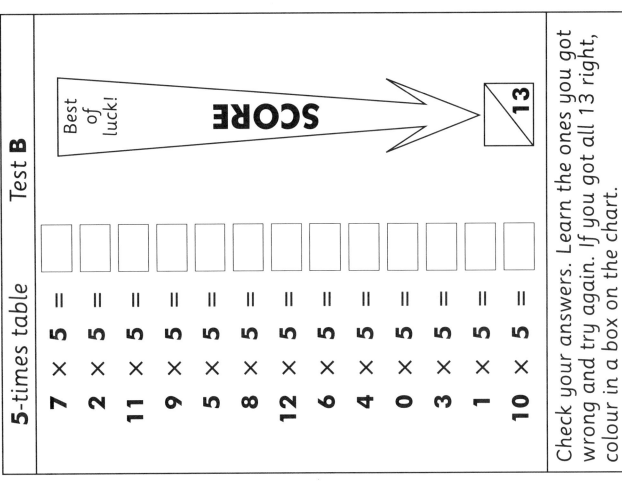

Test B

5-times table

7 × 5 =	
2 × 5 =	
11 × 5 =	
9 × 5 =	
5 × 5 =	
8 × 5 =	
12 × 5 =	
6 × 5 =	
4 × 5 =	
0 × 5 =	
3 × 5 =	
1 × 5 =	
10 × 5 =	

SCORE → 13

Best of luck!

Check your answers. Learn the ones you got wrong and try again. If you got all 13 right, colour in a box on the chart.

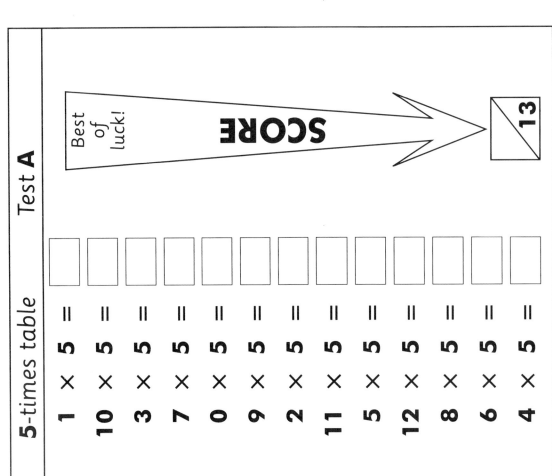

Test A

5-times table

1 × 5 =	
10 × 5 =	
3 × 5 =	
7 × 5 =	
0 × 5 =	
9 × 5 =	
2 × 5 =	
11 × 5 =	
5 × 5 =	
12 × 5 =	
8 × 5 =	
6 × 5 =	
4 × 5 =	

SCORE → 13

Best of luck!

Check your answers. Learn the ones you got wrong and try again. If you got all 13 right, colour in a box on the chart.

Test A		Test B

6-times table — **Test A**

1 × 6 = ☐
10 × 6 = ☐
3 × 6 = ☐
7 × 6 = ☐
0 × 6 = ☐
9 × 6 = ☐
2 × 6 = ☐
11 × 6 = ☐
5 × 6 = ☐
12 × 6 = ☐
8 × 6 = ☐
6 × 6 = ☐
4 × 6 = ☐

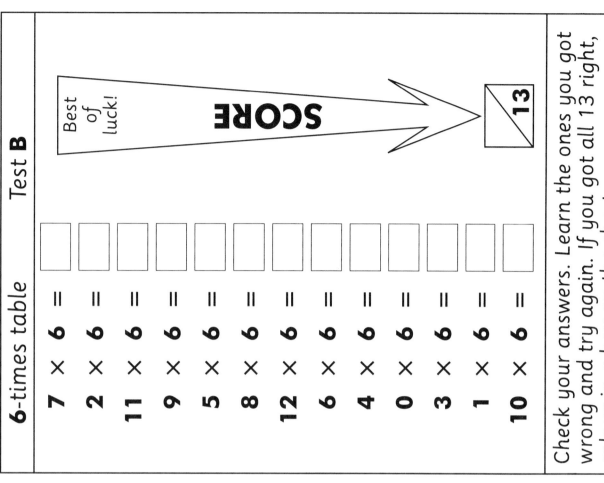

Best of luck!

SCORE ▷ ◁ ⧄ 13

Check your answers. Learn the ones you got wrong and try again. If you got all 13 right, colour in a box on the chart.

6-times table — **Test B**

7 × 6 = ☐
2 × 6 = ☐
11 × 6 = ☐
9 × 6 = ☐
5 × 6 = ☐
8 × 6 = ☐
12 × 6 = ☐
6 × 6 = ☐
4 × 6 = ☐
0 × 6 = ☐
3 × 6 = ☐
1 × 6 = ☐
10 × 6 = ☐

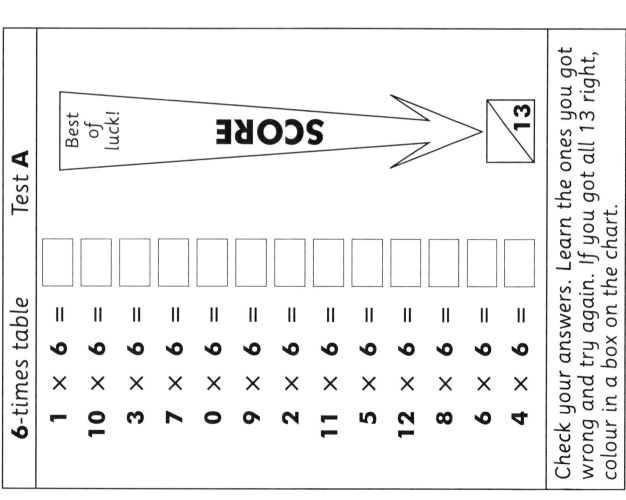

Best of luck!

SCORE ▷ ◁ ⧄ 13

Check your answers. Learn the ones you got wrong and try again. If you got all 13 right, colour in a box on the chart.

Test B

7-times table

SCORE — Best of luck!

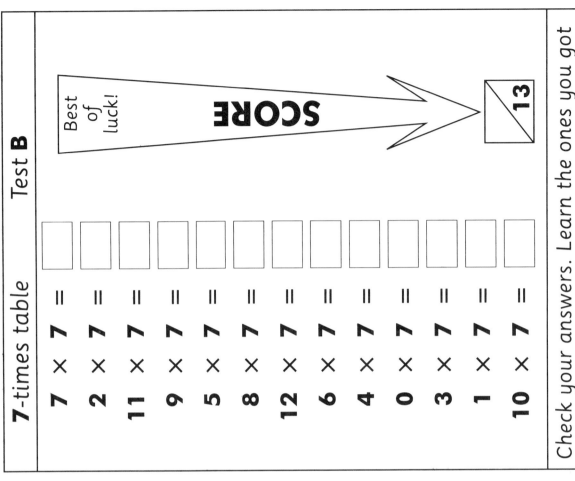

7 × 7 =	
2 × 7 =	
11 × 7 =	
9 × 7 =	
5 × 7 =	
8 × 7 =	
12 × 7 =	
6 × 7 =	
4 × 7 =	
0 × 7 =	
3 × 7 =	
1 × 7 =	
10 × 7 =	

Score: /13

Check your answers. Learn the ones you got wrong and try again. If you got all 13 right, colour in a box on the chart.

Test A

7-times table

SCORE — Best of luck!

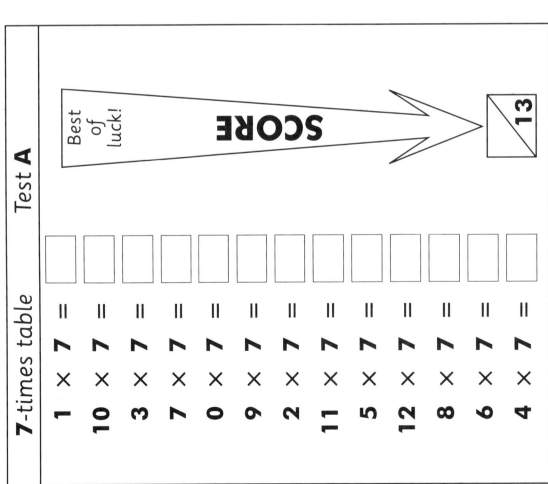

1 × 7 =	
10 × 7 =	
3 × 7 =	
7 × 7 =	
0 × 7 =	
9 × 7 =	
2 × 7 =	
11 × 7 =	
5 × 7 =	
12 × 7 =	
8 × 7 =	
6 × 7 =	
4 × 7 =	

Score: /13

Check your answers. Learn the ones you got wrong and try again. If you got all 13 right, colour in a box on the chart.

Test A

8-times table	
1 × 8 =	
10 × 8 =	
3 × 8 =	
7 × 8 =	
0 × 8 =	
9 × 8 =	
2 × 8 =	
11 × 8 =	
5 × 8 =	
12 × 8 =	
8 × 8 =	
6 × 8 =	
4 × 8 =	

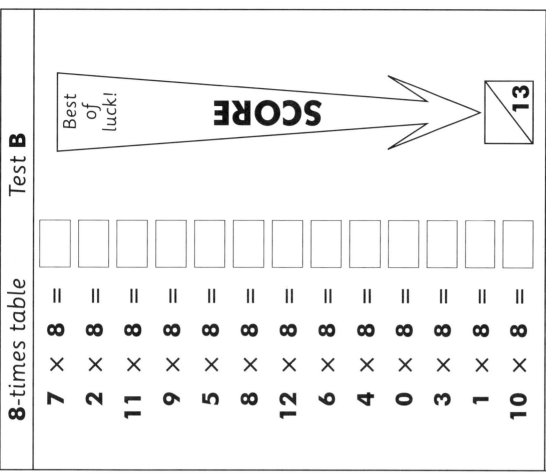

Best of luck!

SCORE

13

Check your answers. Learn the ones you got wrong and try again. If you got all 13 right, colour in a box on the chart.

Test B

8-times table	
7 × 8 =	
2 × 8 =	
11 × 8 =	
9 × 8 =	
5 × 8 =	
8 × 8 =	
12 × 8 =	
6 × 8 =	
4 × 8 =	
0 × 8 =	
3 × 8 =	
1 × 8 =	
10 × 8 =	

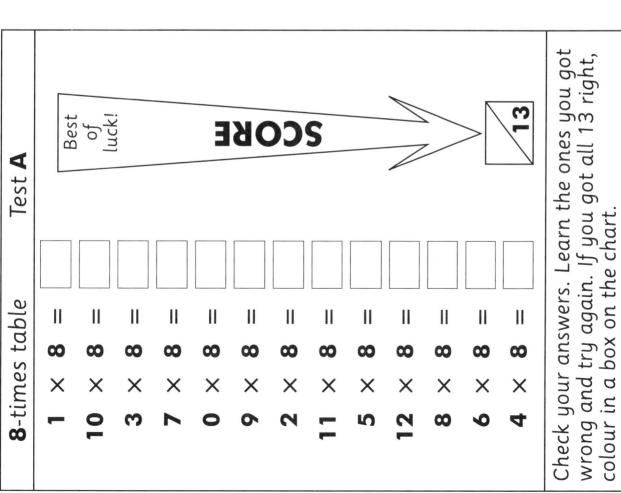

Best of luck!

SCORE

13

Check your answers. Learn the ones you got wrong and try again. If you got all 13 right, colour in a box on the chart.

9-times table — Test B

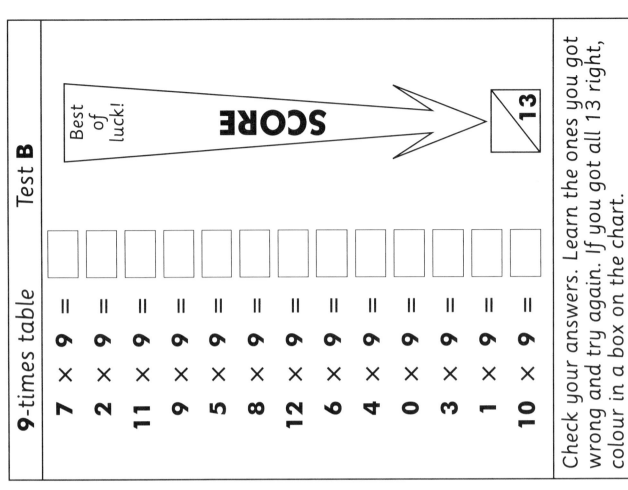

Best of luck!

SCORE → **13**

7 × 9 =	
2 × 9 =	
11 × 9 =	
9 × 9 =	
5 × 9 =	
8 × 9 =	
12 × 9 =	
6 × 9 =	
4 × 9 =	
0 × 9 =	
3 × 9 =	
1 × 9 =	
10 × 9 =	

Check your answers. Learn the ones you got wrong and try again. If you got all 13 right, colour in a box on the chart.

9-times table — Test A

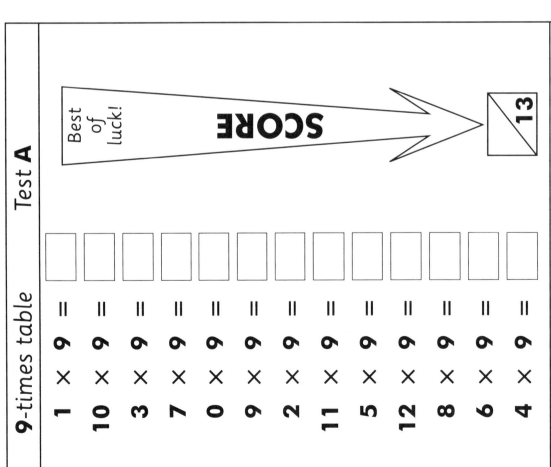

Best of luck!

SCORE → **13**

1 × 9 =	
10 × 9 =	
3 × 9 =	
7 × 9 =	
0 × 9 =	
9 × 9 =	
2 × 9 =	
11 × 9 =	
5 × 9 =	
12 × 9 =	
8 × 9 =	
6 × 9 =	
4 × 9 =	

Check your answers. Learn the ones you got wrong and try again. If you got all 13 right, colour in a box on the chart.

Test A

10-times table

1 × 10 = ☐
10 × 10 = ☐
3 × 10 = ☐
7 × 10 = ☐
0 × 10 = ☐
9 × 10 = ☐
2 × 10 = ☐
11 × 10 = ☐
5 × 10 = ☐
12 × 10 = ☐
8 × 10 = ☐
6 × 10 = ☐
4 × 10 = ☐

SCORE ➤ ☐/13

Best of luck!

Check your answers. Learn the ones you got wrong and try again. If you got all 13 right, colour in a box on the chart.

Test B

10-times table

7 × 10 = ☐
2 × 10 = ☐
11 × 10 = ☐
9 × 10 = ☐
5 × 10 = ☐
8 × 10 = ☐
12 × 10 = ☐
6 × 10 = ☐
4 × 10 = ☐
0 × 10 = ☐
3 × 10 = ☐
1 × 10 = ☐
10 × 10 = ☐

SCORE ➤ ☐/13

Best of luck!

Check your answers. Learn the ones you got wrong and try again. If you got all 13 right, colour in a box on the chart.

Test B

11-times table

7 × 11 =	
2 × 11 =	
11 × 11 =	
9 × 11 =	
5 × 11 =	
8 × 11 =	
12 × 11 =	
6 × 11 =	
4 × 11 =	
0 × 11 =	
3 × 11 =	
1 × 11 =	
10 × 11 =	

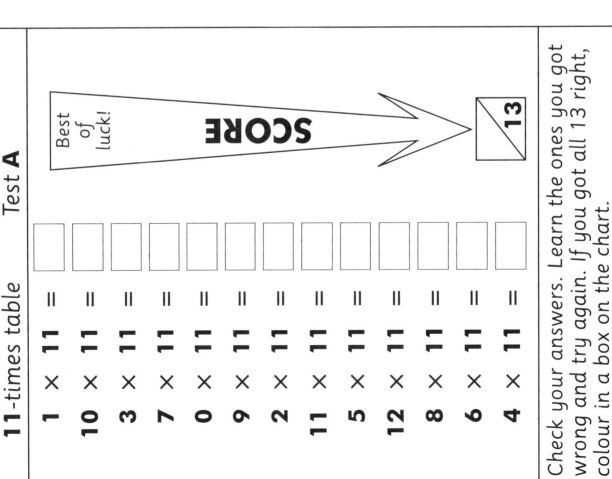

Best of luck!

SCORE

13

Check your answers. Learn the ones you got wrong and try again. If you got all 13 right, colour in a box on the chart.

Test A

11-times table

1 × 11 =	
10 × 11 =	
3 × 11 =	
7 × 11 =	
0 × 11 =	
9 × 11 =	
2 × 11 =	
11 × 11 =	
5 × 11 =	
12 × 11 =	
8 × 11 =	
6 × 11 =	
4 × 11 =	

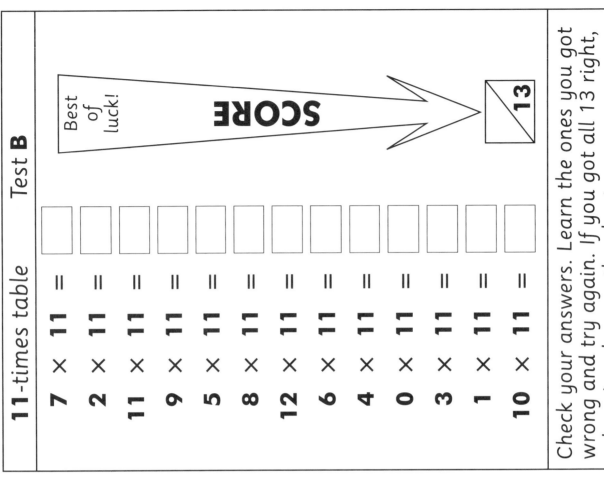

Best of luck!

SCORE

13

Check your answers. Learn the ones you got wrong and try again. If you got all 13 right, colour in a box on the chart.

12-times table　　Test A

1 × 12 = ☐

10 × 12 = ☐

3 × 12 = ☐

7 × 12 = ☐

0 × 12 = ☐

9 × 12 = ☐

2 × 12 = ☐

11 × 12 = ☐

5 × 12 = ☐

12 × 12 = ☐

8 × 12 = ☐

6 × 12 = ☐

4 × 12 = ☐

SCORE

Best of luck!

☐/13

Check your answers. Learn the ones you got wrong and try again. If you got all 13 right, colour in a box on the chart.

12-times table　　Test B

7 × 12 = ☐

2 × 12 = ☐

11 × 12 = ☐

9 × 12 = ☐

5 × 12 = ☐

8 × 12 = ☐

12 × 12 = ☐

6 × 12 = ☐

4 × 12 = ☐

0 × 12 = ☐

3 × 12 = ☐

1 × 12 = ☐

10 × 12 = ☐

SCORE

Best of luck!

☐/13

Check your answers. Learn the ones you got wrong and try again. If you got all 13 right, colour in a box on the chart.

Use your **2**-times table to see if any of these numbers are in the box. Colour the boxes in red and you will see a pattern.

3	5	0	11	3
16	7	14	5	20
12	2	6	4	18
22	11	8	1	24
5	1	10	9	7

Now write your **2**-times table.

0 × **2** =

1 × **2** =

2 × **2** =

3 × **2** =

4 × **2** =

5 × **2** =

6 × **2** =

7 × **2** =

8 × **2** =

9 × **2** =

10 × **2** =

11 × **2** =

12 × **2** =

Can you write it out again without looking?

Tables & Puzzles ?

Use your **3**-times table to see if any of these numbers are in the box. Colour the boxes in red and you will see a pattern.

3	4	8	10	18
14	6	0	21	16
20	36	9	30	34
22	24	33	12	7
27	17	11	19	15

Now write your **3**-times table.

0 × **3** =
1 × **3** =
2 × **3** =
3 × **3** =
4 × **3** =
5 × **3** =
6 × **3** =
7 × **3** =
8 × **3** =
9 × **3** =
10 × **3** =
11 × **3** =
12 × **3** =

Can you write it out again without looking?

Use your **4**-times table to see if any of these numbers are in the box. Colour the boxes in red and you will see a pattern.

8	4	44	32	40
12	9	35	47	36
20	29	11	31	48
16	45	7	13	28
0	8	12	24	16

Now write your **4**-times table.

0 × **4** =
1 × **4** =
2 × **4** =
3 × **4** =
4 × **4** =
5 × **4** =
6 × **4** =
7 × **4** =
8 × **4** =
9 × **4** =
10 × **4** =
11 × **4** =
12 × **4** =

Can you write it out again without looking?

Use your **5**-times table to see if any of these numbers are in the box. Colour the boxes in red and you will see a pattern.

5	55	25	40	0
18	60	24	6	16
49	7	10	57	33
27	51	2	30	8
20	35	50	45	15

Now write your **5**-times table.

0 × 5 =
1 × 5 =
2 × 5 =
3 × 5 =
4 × 5 =
5 × 5 =
6 × 5 =
7 × 5 =
8 × 5 =
9 × 5 =
10 × 5 =
11 × 5 =
12 × 5 =

Can you write it out again without looking?

Use your **6**-times table to see if any of these numbers are in the box. Colour the boxes in red and you will see a pattern.

24	60	30	42	12
21	7	48	28	55
11	1	72	19	8
35	27	54	15	49
36	6	66	0	18

Now write your **6**-times table.

0 × 6 =
1 × 6 =
2 × 6 =
3 × 6 =
4 × 6 =
5 × 6 =
6 × 6 =
7 × 6 =
8 × 6 =
9 × 6 =
10 × 6 =
11 × 6 =
12 × 6 =

Can you write it out again without looking?

7-times table

Use your **7**-times table to see if any of these numbers are in the box. Colour the boxes in red and you will see a pattern.

77	6	7	24	84
20	14	10	21	80
42	5	0	4	28
50	49	3	35	30
63	40	56	69	70

Now write your **7**-times table.

0 × 7 =
1 × 7 =
2 × 7 =
3 × 7 =
4 × 7 =
5 × 7 =
6 × 7 =
7 × 7 =
8 × 7 =
9 × 7 =
10 × 7 =
11 × 7 =
12 × 7 =

Can you write it out again without looking?

8-times table

Use your **8**-times table to see if any of these numbers are in the box. Colour the boxes in red and you will see a pattern.

24	11	1	7	32
40	12	88	9	48
56	10	0	49	64
80	51	96	33	72
16	25	3	50	8

Now write your **8**-times table.

0 × 8 =
1 × 8 =
2 × 8 =
3 × 8 =
4 × 8 =
5 × 8 =
6 × 8 =
7 × 8 =
8 × 8 =
9 × 8 =
10 × 8 =
11 × 8 =
12 × 8 =

Can you write it out again without looking?

Use your **10**-times table to see if any of these numbers are in the box. Colour the boxes in red and you will see a pattern.

0	35	49	63	110
8	20	120	100	6
3	60	10	70	15
11	40	90	30	5
50	27	31	9	80

Now write your **10**-times table.

0 × 10 =
1 × 10 =
2 × 10 =
3 × 10 =
4 × 10 =
5 × 10 =
6 × 10 =
7 × 10 =
8 × 10 =
9 × 10 =
10 × 10 =
11 × 10 =
12 × 10 =

Can you write it out again without looking?

Use your **9**-times table to see if any of these numbers are in the box. Colour the boxes in red and you will see a pattern.

8	6	108	12	80
15	60	0	100	13
24	25	99	10	70
27	63	54	81	18
9	45	72	90	36

Now write your **9**-times table.

0 × 9 =
1 × 9 =
2 × 9 =
3 × 9 =
4 × 9 =
5 × 9 =
6 × 9 =
7 × 9 =
8 × 9 =
9 × 9 =
10 × 9 =
11 × 9 =
12 × 9 =

Can you write it out again without looking?

Use your **11**-times table to see if any of these numbers are in the box. Colour the boxes in red and you will see a pattern.

44	88	110	66	22
45	54	31	32	34
9	121	0	99	8
5	76	100	101	19
132	33	77	11	55

Now write your **11**-times table.

0 × 11 =
1 × 11 =
2 × 11 =
3 × 11 =
4 × 11 =
5 × 11 =
6 × 11 =
7 × 11 =
8 × 11 =
9 × 11 =
10 × 11 =
11 × 11 =
12 × 11 =

Can you write it out again without looking?

Use your **12**-times table to see if any of these numbers are in the box. Colour the boxes in red and you will see a pattern.

48	16	7	39	84
96	24	8	5	120
132	13	60	90	144
0	11	61	36	72
12	51	41	99	108

Now write your **12**-times table.

0 × 12 =
1 × 12 =
2 × 12 =
3 × 12 =
4 × 12 =
5 × 12 =
6 × 12 =
7 × 12 =
8 × 12 =
9 × 12 =
10 × 12 =
11 × 12 =
12 × 12 =

Can you write it out again without looking?

Choose a table and make a puzzle for your friends to solve.

Now write your ☐-times table.

0 ×	=	
1 ×	=	
2 ×	=	
3 ×	=	
4 ×	=	
5 ×	=	
6 ×	=	
7 ×	=	
8 ×	=	
9 ×	=	
10 ×	=	
11 ×	=	
12 ×	=	

Can you write it out again without looking?

Choose a table and make a puzzle for your friends to solve.

Now write your ☐-times table.

0 ×	=	
1 ×	=	
2 ×	=	
3 ×	=	
4 ×	=	
5 ×	=	
6 ×	=	
7 ×	=	
8 ×	=	
9 ×	=	
10 ×	=	
11 ×	=	
12 ×	=	

Can you write it out again without looking?

Thinking backwards

1×2 =
9×3 =
4×3 =

5×6 =
12×12 =
8×4 =
9×9 =
6×6 =

11×1 =
3×10 =
10×7 =

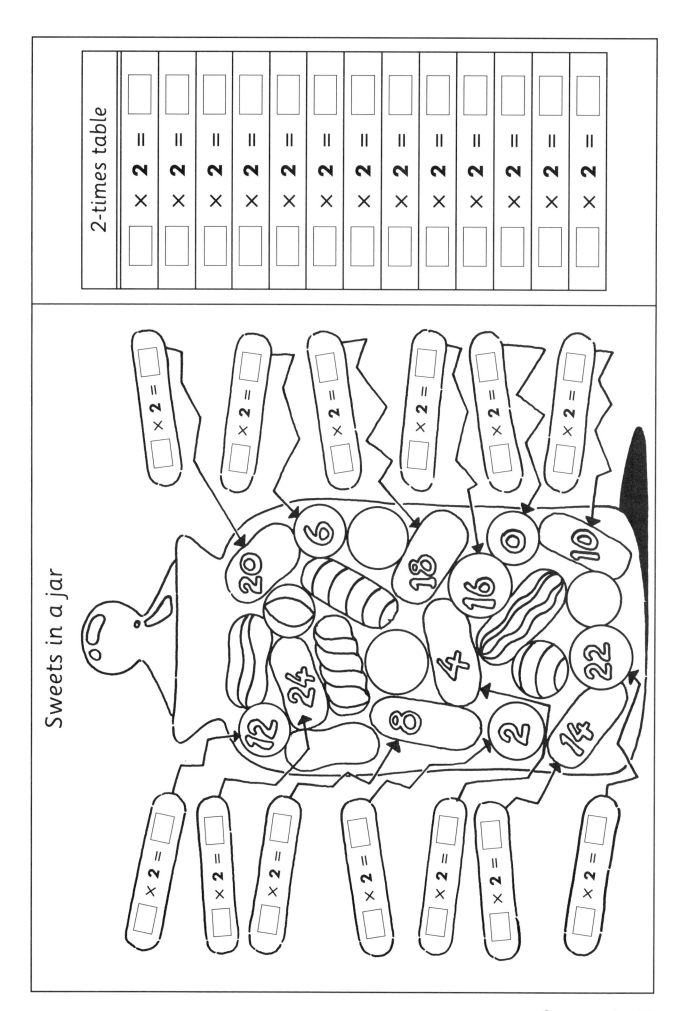

Sweets in a jar

2-times table

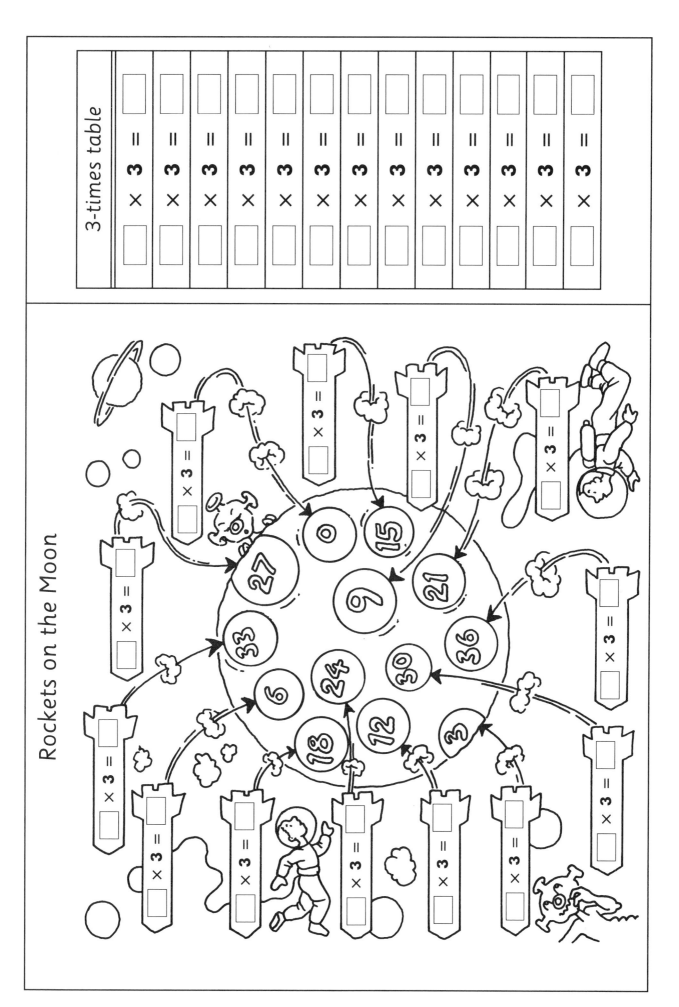

Rockets on the Moon

3-times table

4-times table

	×	4	=	
	×	4	=	
	×	4	=	
	×	4	=	
	×	4	=	
	×	4	=	
	×	4	=	
	×	4	=	
	×	4	=	
	×	4	=	
	×	4	=	
	×	4	=	
	×	4	=	

Windows on a submarine

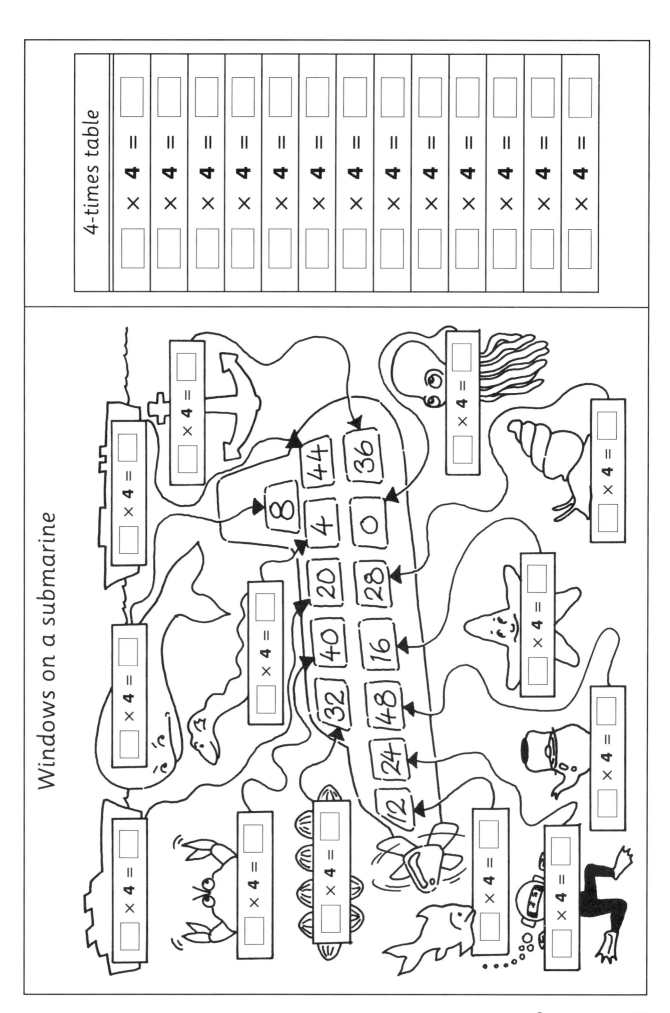

5-times table

☐	× **5** =	☐
☐	× **5** =	☐
☐	× **5** =	☐
☐	× **5** =	☐
☐	× **5** =	☐
☐	× **5** =	☐
☐	× **5** =	☐
☐	× **5** =	☐
☐	× **5** =	☐
☐	× **5** =	☐
☐	× **5** =	☐
☐	× **5** =	☐
☐	× **5** =	☐

Pirate treasure

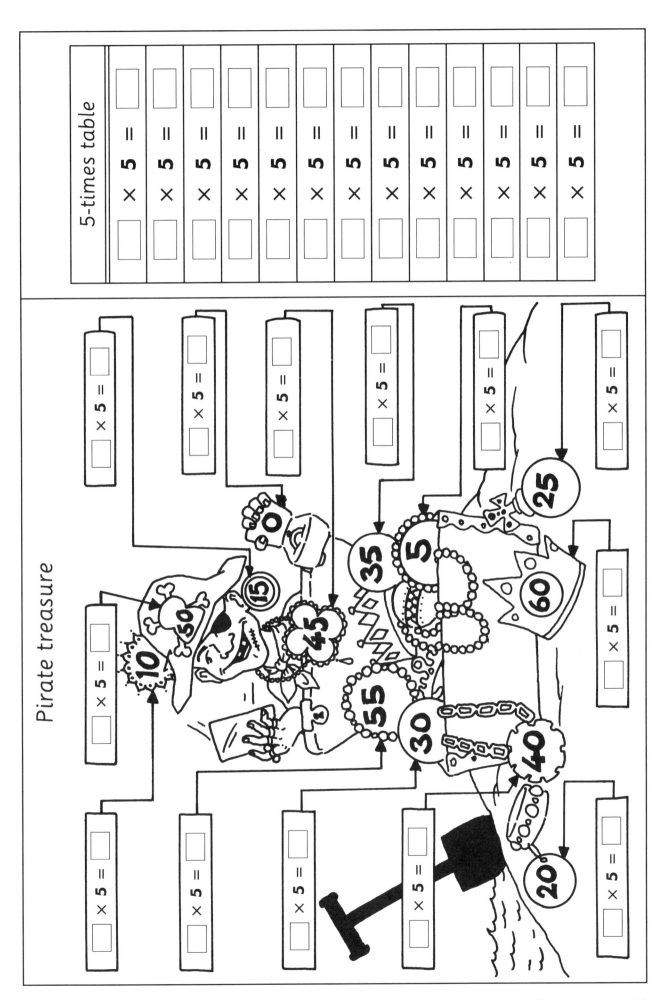

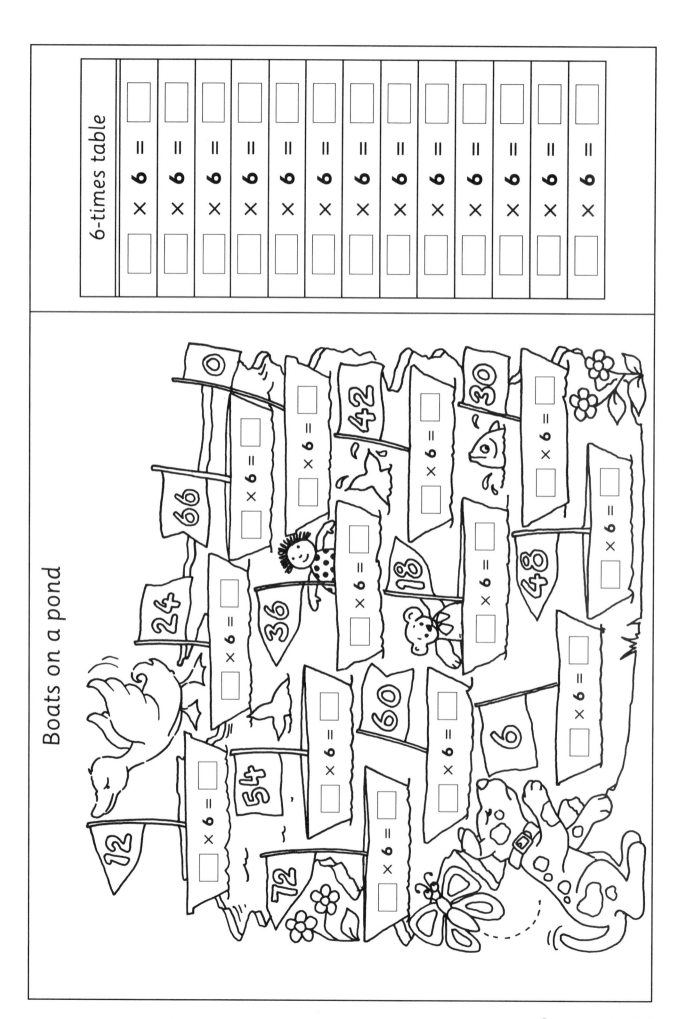

6-times table

Boats on a pond

7-times table

☐	×	**7** =	☐
☐	×	**7** =	☐
☐	×	**7** =	☐
☐	×	**7** =	☐
☐	×	**7** =	☐
☐	×	**7** =	☐
☐	×	**7** =	☐
☐	×	**7** =	☐
☐	×	**7** =	☐
☐	×	**7** =	☐
☐	×	**7** =	☐
☐	×	**7** =	☐

Runners in a race

8-times table

	× 8 =			
	× 8 =			
	× 8 =			
	× 8 =			
	× 8 =			
	× 8 =			
	× 8 =			
	× 8 =			
	× 8 =			
	× 8 =			
	× 8 =			
	× 8 =			
	× 8 =			

Flowers in pots

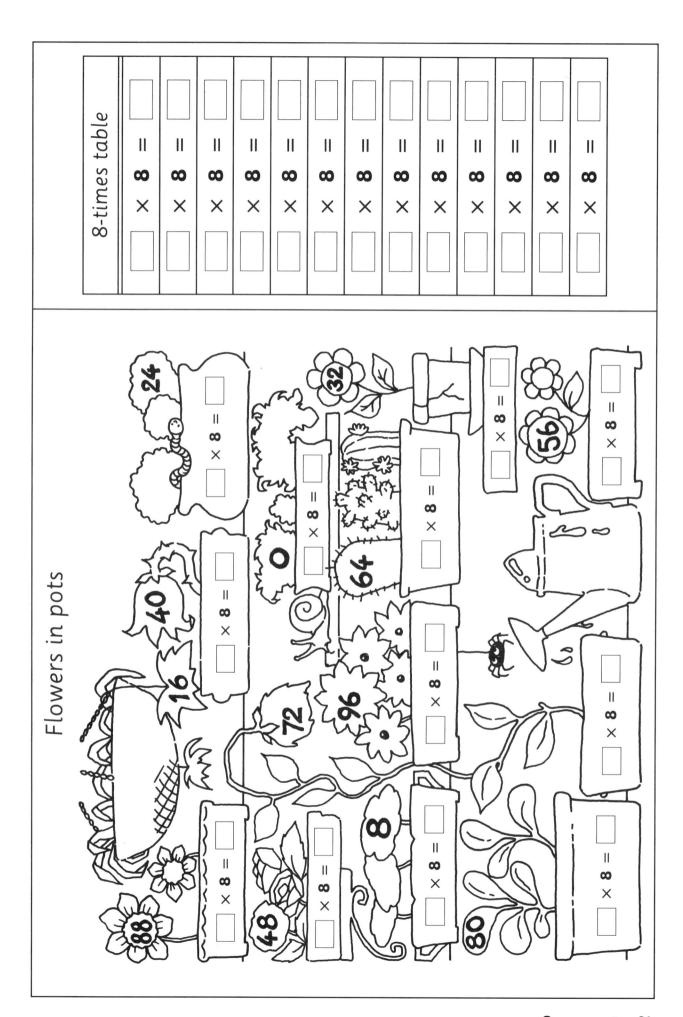

9-times table

		☐
☐ × 9 =		☐
☐ × 9 =		☐
☐ × 9 =		☐
☐ × 9 =		☐
☐ × 9 =		☐
☐ × 9 =		☐
☐ × 9 =		☐
☐ × 9 =		☐
☐ × 9 =		☐
☐ × 9 =		☐
☐ × 9 =		☐
☐ × 9 =		☐
☐ × 9 =		☐

Squirrels up a tree

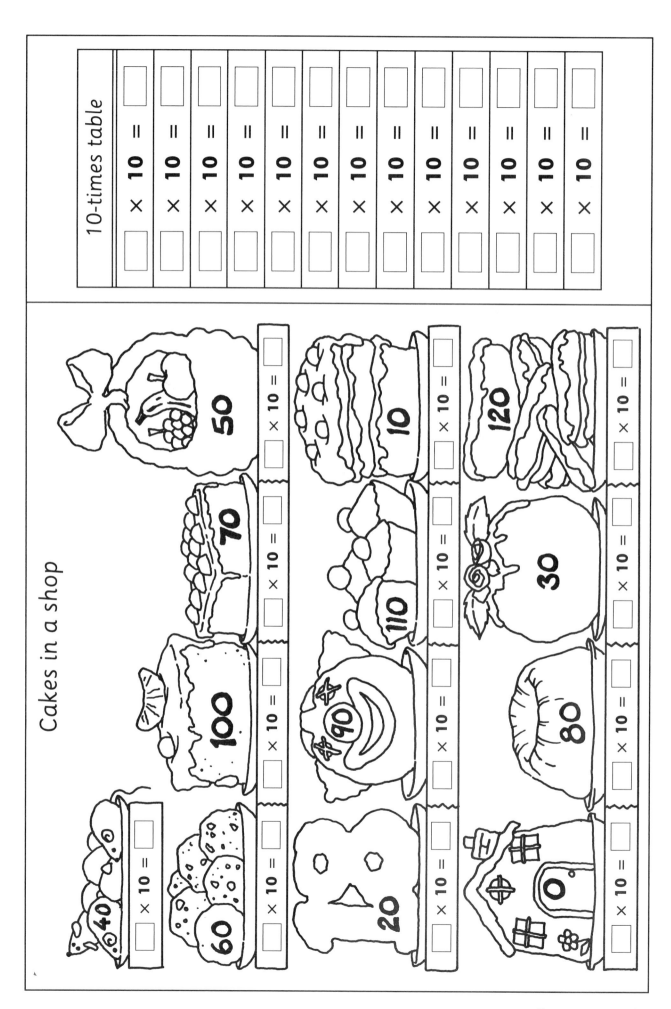

10-times table

☐	× **10**	=	☐
☐	× **10**	=	☐
☐	× **10**	=	☐
☐	× **10**	=	☐
☐	× **10**	=	☐
☐	× **10**	=	☐
☐	× **10**	=	☐
☐	× **10**	=	☐
☐	× **10**	=	☐
☐	× **10**	=	☐
☐	× **10**	=	☐
☐	× **10**	=	☐
☐	× **10**	=	☐

Cakes in a shop

☐ × 10 = ☐   40
☐ × 10 = ☐   60
☐ × 10 = ☐   100
☐ × 10 = ☐   70
☐ × 10 = ☐   50

☐ × 10 = ☐   20
☐ × 10 = ☐   90
☐ × 10 = ☐   110
☐ × 10 = ☐   10

☐ × 10 = ☐   0
☐ × 10 = ☐   80
☐ × 10 = ☐   30
☐ × 10 = ☐   120

Mice and cheese

11-times table

☐	× 11	=	☐
☐	× 11	=	☐
☐	× 11	=	☐
☐	× 11	=	☐
☐	× 11	=	☐
☐	× 11	=	☐
☐	× 11	=	☐
☐	× 11	=	☐
☐	× 11	=	☐
☐	× 11	=	☐
☐	× 11	=	☐
☐	× 11	=	☐
☐	× 11	=	☐

Room with a view

12-times table

	× 12 =	
	× 12 =	
	× 12 =	
	× 12 =	
	× 12 =	
	× 12 =	
	× 12 =	
	× 12 =	
	× 12 =	
	× 12 =	
	× 12 =	
	× 12 =	

1-times table
slider card

Test →

CUT THIS SECTION OUT	Questions		CUT THIS SECTION OUT	Answers
	× 1 =			
	× 1 =			
	× 1 =			
	× 1 =			
	× 1 =			
	× 1 =			
	× 1 =			
	× 1 =			
	× 1 =			
	× 1 =			
	× 1 =			
	× 1 =			

Test →

Learn the ones you get wrong and try again.

2-times table
slider card

CUT THIS SECTION OUT	Questions		CUT THIS SECTION OUT	Answers
	× 2 =			
	× 2 =			
	× 2 =			
	× 2 =			
	× 2 =			
	× 2 =			
	× 2 =			
	× 2 =			
	× 2 =			
	× 2 =			
	× 2 =			
	× 2 =			

Test →

Learn the ones you get wrong and try again.

3-times table
slider card

Test ➤

Questions			Answers
× **3** =			
× **3** =			
× **3** =			
× **3** =			
× **3** =			
× **3** =			
× **3** =			
× **3** =			
× **3** =			
× **3** =			
× **3** =			
× **3** =			

CUT THIS SECTION OUT

CUT THIS SECTION OUT

Learn the ones you get wrong and try again.

4-times table
slider card

Questions			Answers
× **4** =			
× **4** =			
× **4** =			
× **4** =			
× **4** =			
× **4** =			
× **4** =			
× **4** =			
× **4** =			
× **4** =			
× **4** =			
× **4** =			

CUT THIS SECTION OUT

CUT THIS SECTION OUT

Learn the ones you get wrong and try again.

5-times table
slider card

Test ➤		Questions	Test ➤		Answers

CUT THIS SECTION OUT

× 5 =
× 5 =
× 5 =
× 5 =
× 5 =
× 5 =
× 5 =
× 5 =
× 5 =
× 5 =
× 5 =
× 5 =

CUT THIS SECTION OUT

Learn the ones you get wrong and try again.

6-times table
slider card

Test ➤		Questions	Test ➤		Answers

CUT THIS SECTION OUT

× 6 =
× 6 =
× 6 =
× 6 =
× 6 =
× 6 =
× 6 =
× 6 =
× 6 =
× 6 =
× 6 =
× 6 =

CUT THIS SECTION OUT

Learn the ones you get wrong and try again.

7-times table
slider card

Test ▷

CUT THIS SECTION OUT

Questions	
× **7** =	
× **7** =	
× **7** =	
× **7** =	
× **7** =	
× **7** =	
× **7** =	
× **7** =	
× **7** =	
× **7** =	
× **7** =	
× **7** =	

Test ▷

CUT THIS SECTION OUT

Answers

Learn the ones you get wrong and try again.

8-times table
slider card

Test ▷

CUT THIS SECTION OUT

Questions	
× **8** =	
× **8** =	
× **8** =	
× **8** =	
× **8** =	
× **8** =	
× **8** =	
× **8** =	
× **8** =	
× **8** =	
× **8** =	
× **8** =	

Test ▷

CUT THIS SECTION OUT

Answers

Learn the ones you get wrong and try again.

9-times table
slider card

Test →

Questions		Answers
× 9 =		
× 9 =		
× 9 =		
× 9 =		
× 9 =		
× 9 =		
× 9 =		
× 9 =		
× 9 =		
× 9 =		
× 9 =		
× 9 =		

CUT THIS SECTION OUT

CUT THIS SECTION OUT

Learn the ones you get wrong and try again.

10-times table
slider card

Test →

Questions		Answers
× 10 =		
× 10 =		
× 10 =		
× 10 =		
× 10 =		
× 10 =		
× 10 =		
× 10 =		
× 10 =		
× 10 =		
× 10 =		
× 10 =		

CUT THIS SECTION OUT

CUT THIS SECTION OUT

Learn the ones you get wrong and try again.

11-times table
slider card

Test ⟩

CUT THIS SECTION OUT

Questions		Test ⟩		Answers
× 11 =				
× 11 =				
× 11 =				
× 11 =				
× 11 =				
× 11 =				
× 11 =				
× 11 =				
× 11 =				
× 11 =				
× 11 =				
× 11 =				

CUT THIS SECTION OUT

Learn the ones you get wrong and try again.

12-times table
slider card

CUT THIS SECTION OUT

Questions		Test ⟩		Answers
× 12 =				
× 12 =				
× 12 =				
× 12 =				
× 12 =				
× 12 =				
× 12 =				
× 12 =				
× 12 =				
× 12 =				
× 12 =				
× 12 =				

CUT THIS SECTION OUT

Learn the ones you get wrong and try again.

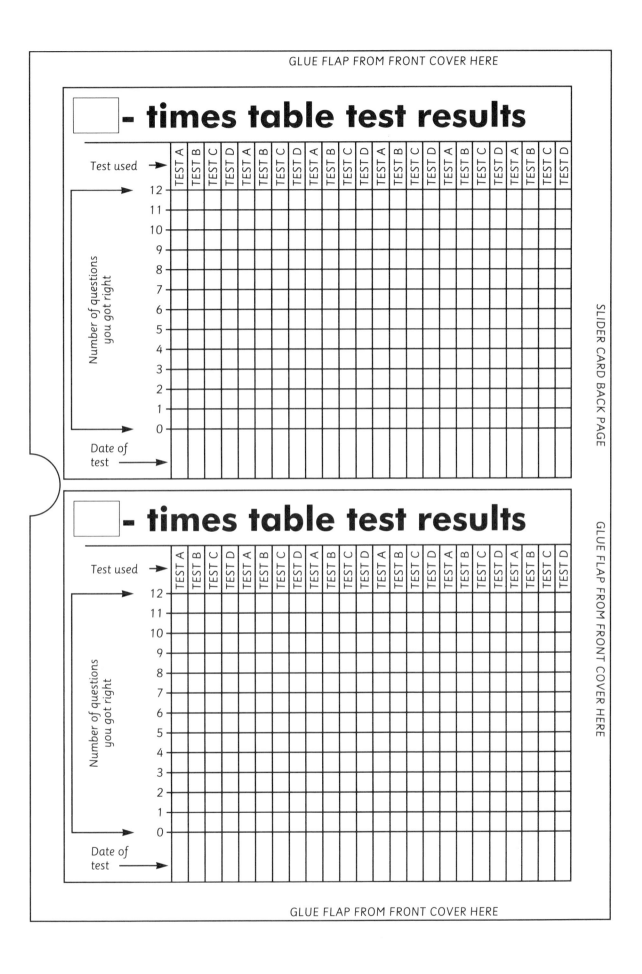

D	C	B	A	D	C	B	A
3	2	9	4	3	2	9	4
8	6	5	1	8	6	5	1
2	12	7	11	2	12	7	11
6	4	10	9	6	4	10	9
12	1	3	5	12	1	3	5
4	11	8	7	4	11	8	7
1	9	2	10	1	9	2	10
11	5	6	3	11	5	6	3
9	7	12	8	9	7	12	8
5	10	4	2	5	10	4	2
7	3	1	6	7	3	1	6
10	8	11	12	10	8	11	12

PULL

2-times table slider

D	C	B	A	D	C	B	A
3	2	9	4	6	4	18	8
8	6	5	1	16	12	10	2
2	12	7	11	4	24	14	22
6	4	10	9	12	8	20	18
12	1	3	5	24	2	6	10
4	11	8	7	8	22	16	14
1	9	2	10	2	18	4	20
11	5	6	3	22	10	12	6
9	7	12	8	18	14	24	16
7	3	1	6	14	6	2	12
10	8	11	12	20	16	22	24
5	10	4	2	10	20	8	4

D	C	B	A	D	C	B	A
3	2	9	4	9	6	27	12
8	6	5	1	24	18	15	3
2	12	7	11	6	36	21	33
6	4	10	9	18	12	30	27
12	1	3	5	36	3	9	15
4	11	8	7	12	33	24	21
1	9	2	10	3	27	6	30
11	5	6	3	33	15	18	9
9	7	12	8	27	21	36	24
5	10	4	2	15	30	12	6
7	3	1	6	21	9	3	18
10	8	11	12	30	24	33	36

3-times table slider

PULL

D	C	B	A	D	C	B	A
3	2	9	4	12	8	36	16
8	6	5	1	32	24	20	4
2	12	7	11	8	48	28	44
6	4	10	9	24	16	40	36
12	1	3	5	48	4	12	20
4	11	8	7	16	44	32	28
1	9	2	10	4	36	8	40
11	5	6	3	44	20	24	12
9	7	12	8	36	28	48	32
7	3	1	6	28	12	4	24
10	8	11	12	40	32	44	48
5	10	4	2	20	40	16	8

4-times table slider

5-times table slider

D	C	B	A	D	C	B	A
3	2	9	4	15	10	45	20
8	6	5	1	40	30	25	5
2	12	7	11	10	60	35	55
6	4	10	9	30	20	50	45
12	1	3	5	60	5	15	25
4	11	8	7	20	55	40	35
1	9	2	10	5	45	10	50
11	5	6	3	55	25	30	15
9	7	12	8	45	35	60	40
5	10	4	2	25	50	20	10
7	3	1	6	35	15	5	30
10	8	11	12	50	40	55	60

PULL

6-times table slider

D	C	B	A	D	C	B	A
3	2	9	4	18	12	54	24
8	6	5	1	48	36	30	6
2	12	7	11	12	72	42	66
6	4	10	9	36	24	60	54
12	1	3	5	72	6	18	30
4	11	8	7	24	66	48	42
1	9	2	10	6	54	12	60
11	5	6	3	66	30	36	18
9	7	12	8	54	42	72	48
7	3	1	6	42	18	6	36
10	8	11	12	60	48	66	72
5	10	4	2	30	60	24	12

7-times table slider

D	C	B	A	D	C	B	A
3	2	9	4	21	14	63	28
8	6	5	1	56	42	35	7
2	12	7	11	14	84	49	77
6	4	10	9	42	28	70	63
12	1	3	5	84	7	21	35
4	11	8	7	28	77	56	49
1	9	2	10	7	63	14	70
11	5	6	3	77	35	42	21
9	7	12	8	63	49	84	56
5	10	4	2	35	70	28	14
7	3	1	6	49	21	7	42
10	8	11	12	70	56	77	84

PULL

8-times table slider

D	C	B	A	D	C	B	A
3	2	9	4	24	16	72	32
8	6	5	1	64	48	40	8
2	12	7	11	16	96	56	88
6	4	10	9	48	32	80	72
12	1	3	5	96	8	24	40
4	11	8	7	32	88	64	56
1	9	2	10	8	72	16	80
11	5	6	3	88	40	48	24
9	7	12	8	72	56	96	64
7	3	1	6	56	24	8	48
10	8	11	12	80	64	88	96
5	10	4	2	40	80	32	16

9-times table slider

D	C	B	A	D	C	B	A
3	2	9	4	27	18	81	36
8	6	5	1	72	54	45	9
2	12	7	11	18	108	63	99
6	4	10	9	54	36	90	81
12	1	3	5	108	9	27	45
4	11	8	7	36	99	72	63
1	9	2	10	9	81	18	90
11	5	6	3	99	45	54	27
9	7	12	8	81	63	108	72
5	10	4	2	45	90	36	18
7	3	1	6	63	27	9	54
10	8	11	12	90	72	99	108

PULL

10-times table slider

D	C	B	A	D	C	B	A
3	2	9	4	30	20	90	40
8	6	5	1	80	60	50	10
2	12	7	11	20	120	70	110
6	4	10	9	60	40	100	90
12	1	3	5	120	10	30	50
4	11	8	7	40	110	80	70
1	9	2	10	10	90	20	100
11	5	6	3	110	50	60	30
9	7	12	8	90	70	120	80
7	3	1	6	70	30	10	60
10	8	11	12	100	80	110	120
5	10	4	2	50	100	40	20

D	C	B	A	D	C	B	A
3	2	9	4	33	22	99	44
8	6	5	1	88	66	55	11
2	12	7	11	22	132	77	121
6	4	10	9	66	44	110	99
12	1	3	5	132	11	33	55
4	11	8	7	44	121	88	77
1	9	2	10	11	99	22	110
11	5	6	3	121	55	66	33
9	7	12	8	99	77	132	88
5	10	4	2	55	110	44	22
7	3	1	6	77	33	11	66
10	8	11	12	110	88	121	132

11-times table slider

PULL

12-times table slider

D	C	B	A	D	C	B	A
3	2	9	4	36	24	108	48
8	6	5	1	96	72	60	12
2	12	7	11	24	144	84	132
6	4	10	9	72	48	120	108
12	1	3	5	144	12	36	60
4	11	8	7	48	132	96	84
1	9	2	10	12	108	24	120
11	5	6	3	132	60	72	36
9	7	12	8	108	84	144	96
7	3	1	6	84	36	12	72
10	8	11	12	120	96	132	144
5	10	4	2	60	120	48	24

Tables grid C

9	2	11	5	0	6	3	12	1	4	8	10	7

8
4
10
12
3
6
0
5
11
2
9
7
1

✂ Cut out this section ✂

Off you go!

Tables grid D

0	6	3	4	1	12	7	10	8	11	2	9	5

11
2
9
5
0
6
3
4
1
12
7
10
8

✂ Cut out this section ✂

Off you go!

Tables grid A Answers

21	6	27	12	30	3	24	0	33	9	15	36	18
35	10	45	20	50	5	40	0	55	15	25	60	30
84	24	108	48	120	12	96	0	132	36	60	144	72
42	12	54	24	60	6	48	0	66	18	30	72	36
49	14	63	28	70	7	56	0	77	21	35	84	42
14	4	18	8	20	2	16	0	22	6	10	24	12
63	18	81	36	90	9	72	0	99	27	45	108	54
28	8	36	16	40	4	32	0	44	12	20	48	24
77	22	99	44	110	11	88	0	121	33	55	132	66
0	0	0	0	0	0	0	0	0	0	0	0	0
56	16	72	32	80	8	64	0	88	24	40	96	48
7	2	9	4	10	1	8	0	11	3	5	12	6
70	20	90	40	100	10	80	0	110	30	50	120	60

Tables grid B Answers

88	110	99	77	132	33	0	11	44	22	66	55	121
40	50	45	35	60	15	0	5	20	10	30	25	55
48	60	54	42	72	18	0	6	24	12	36	30	66
16	20	18	14	24	6	0	2	8	4	12	10	22
32	40	36	28	48	12	0	4	16	8	24	20	44
8	10	9	7	12	3	0	1	4	2	6	5	11
0	0	0	0	0	0	0	0	0	0	0	0	0
24	30	27	21	36	9	0	3	12	6	18	15	33
96	120	108	84	144	36	0	12	48	24	72	60	132
56	70	63	49	84	21	0	7	28	14	42	35	77
72	90	81	63	108	27	0	9	36	18	54	45	99
80	100	90	70	120	30	0	10	40	20	60	50	110
64	80	72	56	96	24	0	8	32	16	48	40	88

Tables grid C

Answers

72	16	88	40	0	48	24	96	8	32	64	80	56
36	8	44	20	0	24	12	48	4	16	32	40	28
90	20	110	50	0	60	30	120	10	40	80	100	70
108	24	132	60	0	72	36	144	12	48	96	120	84
27	6	33	15	0	18	9	36	3	12	24	30	21
54	12	66	30	0	36	18	72	6	24	48	60	42
0	0	0	0	0	0	0	0	0	0	0	0	0
45	10	55	25	0	30	15	60	5	20	40	50	35
99	22	121	55	0	66	33	132	11	44	88	110	77
18	4	22	10	0	12	6	24	2	8	16	20	14
81	18	99	45	0	54	27	108	9	36	72	90	63
63	14	77	35	0	42	21	84	7	28	56	70	49
9	2	11	5	0	6	3	12	1	4	8	10	7

Tables grid D

Answers

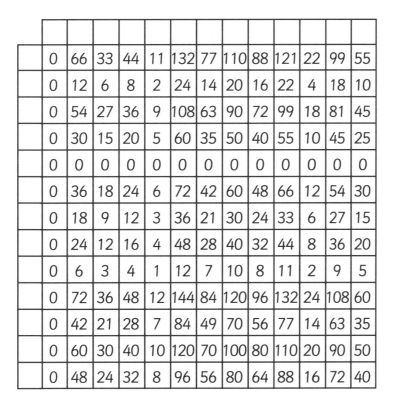

0	66	33	44	11	132	77	110	88	121	22	99	55
0	12	6	8	2	24	14	20	16	22	4	18	10
0	54	27	36	9	108	63	90	72	99	18	81	45
0	30	15	20	5	60	35	50	40	55	10	45	25
0	0	0	0	0	0	0	0	0	0	0	0	0
0	36	18	24	6	72	42	60	48	66	12	54	30
0	18	9	12	3	36	21	30	24	33	6	27	15
0	24	12	16	4	48	28	40	32	44	8	36	20
0	6	3	4	1	12	7	10	8	11	2	9	5
0	72	36	48	12	144	84	120	96	132	24	108	60
0	42	21	28	7	84	49	70	56	77	14	63	35
0	60	30	40	10	120	70	100	80	110	20	90	50
0	48	24	32	8	96	56	80	64	88	16	72	40

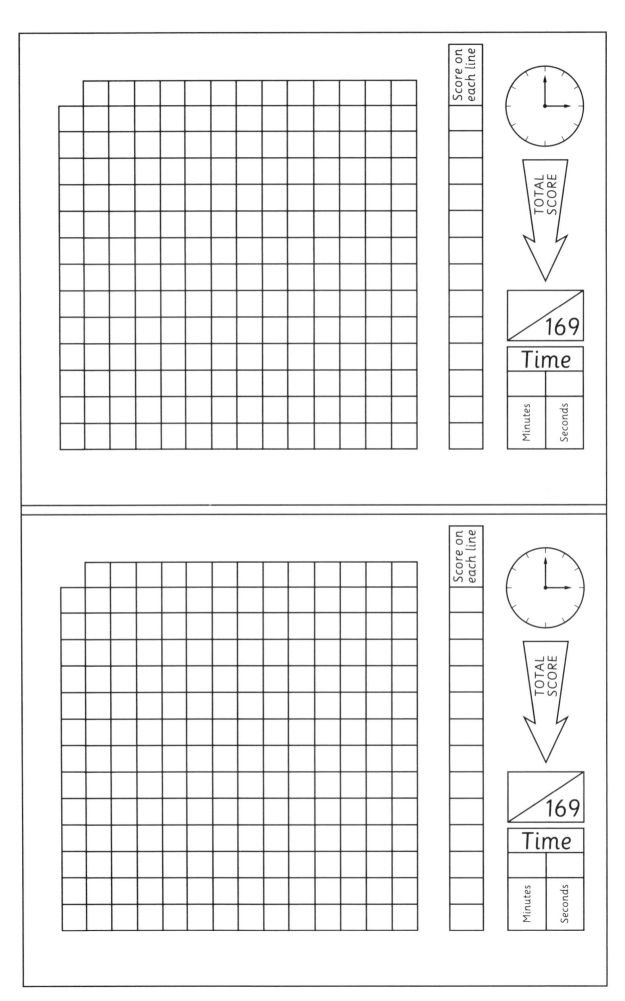

Score on each line

TOTAL SCORE

169

Time

Minutes | Seconds

Score on each line

TOTAL SCORE

169

Time

Minutes | Seconds

Copymaster 116

Your progress graph

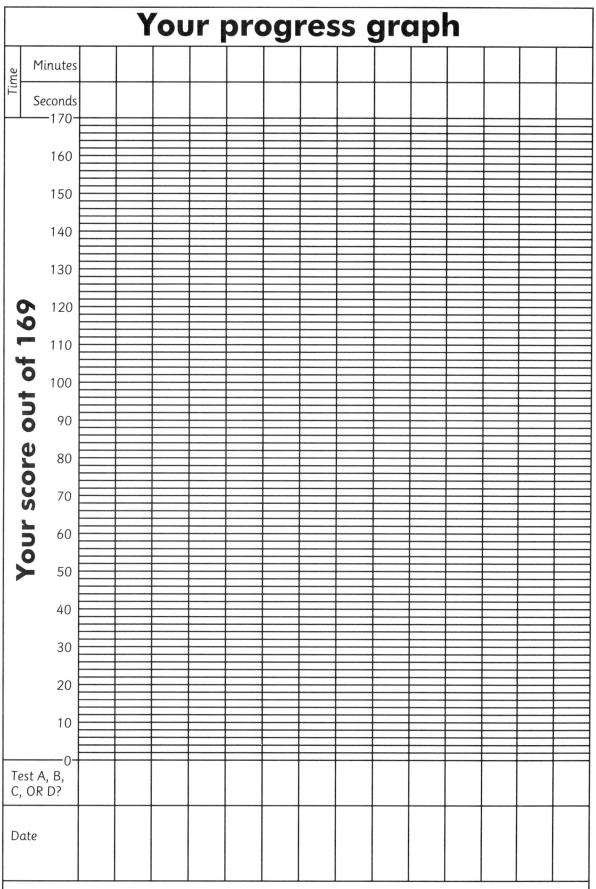

Time — Minutes / Seconds

Your score out of 169

170
160
150
140
130
120
110
100
90
80
70
60
50
40
30
20
10
0

Test A, B, C, OR D?

Date

Record your results for each test you do.
Learn the ones you get wrong and try again.

Skill levels

Score **169** right answers and beat these times

Less than 15 minutes ...	Personal best
Less than 14 minutes ...	Class champion
Less than 13 minutes ...	School champion
Less than 12 minutes ...	Area champion
Less than 11 minutes ...	County champion
Less than 10 minutes ...	National champion
Less than 9 minutes ...	Olympic champion
Less than 8 minutes ...	World champion
Less than 7 minutes ...	Solar System champion
Less than 6 minutes ...	Universe champion
Less than 5 minutes ...	Impossible!

Colour in the medals as you win them.

PERSONAL ~BEST~ CLASS CHAMPION SCHOOL CHAMPION AREA CHAMPION COUNTY CHAMPION

NATIONAL CHAMPION OLYMPIC CHAMPION WORLD CHAMPION SOLAR SYSTEM CHAMPION UNIVERSE CHAMPION

I've done °THE° IMPOSSIBLE I'm great!